UNIVERSE-SUPPORTED REVOLUTION

6-Week Planner + Spiritual Guide = Daily Freedom

AM/PM
Ocean Blue

Phoenix G., MBA

Sunshine Under the Trees, Corporation

Sugar Land, Texas, USA

For information about special discounts for bulk purchases, please visit UniverseSupportedRevolution.com

English
AM/PM
Undated
6-Weeks
Size A5 (5.83 x 8.27 in) (148 x 210 mm)
Perfect Bound Binding
White Paper
Paper Weight (50 lb) (74 gsm)
Paperback Cover
Cover Color: Ocean Blue

Sunshine Under the Trees, Corporation
P.O. Box 1568
Sugar Land, TX, 77487-1568 USA
www.UniverseSupportedRevolution.com

Book Layout © 2017 BookDesignTemplates.com

Cover Art © 2022 Sunshine Under the Trees, Corporation

Universe-Supported Revolution: 6-Week Planner + Spiritual Guide = Daily Freedom. AM/PM. Ocean Blue / Phoenix G., MBA. -- 1st ed.
ISBN 978-0-578-35758-4

DEDICATION

I Channel the Energy of the Universe

{Talking to Self}: I'm so proud of you, sweetheart

To my family who never gave up on me

To my fellows who gently encouraged me to be positively visible

The pessimist complains about the wind, the optimist expects it to change, and the leader adjusts the sails.

—JOHN MAXWELL

CONTENTS

THIS PLANNER BELONGS TO...9

WARNING 11

REVOLUTION 13

HOW DO I USE THIS PLANNER? 17

    TRACK DATA 17

    GENTLE PLAN..19

    I'M SO PROUD OF YOU FOR… 19

    MINI ACTIONS FOR MINI GOALS 20

    I CHANNEL THE ENERGY OF THE UNIVERSE! 23

    I DO MY BEST AND I TAKE REST 24

    MULTI-TASKING 25

    TIME HOSTAGES 25

    DAILY JOURNALING 27

    MAX TIMES 29

    GENTLE TIME HONESTY 30

    ALARMS ....3⁓

    WHAT DO YOU NEED RIGHT MEOW? ....

    AFTER TIME, MORE DETAILED ....

UNIVERSE-SUPPORTED......................................

WIDER GENTLE PLAN: 6-WEEKS ....

GENTLE WEEK PLANNING: REMEMBᵣ

GENTLE WEEK 1.................................

GENTLE WEEK 2................................

GENTLE WEEK 3..99

GENTLE WEEK 4..115

GENTLE WEEK 5..131

GENTLE WEEK 6..147

GENTLE DATA 163

GUIDED MEDITATION 169

COUNTRY OF THE DAY...175

UNIVERSE-SUPPORTED TEAM 181

ABOUT THE AUTHOR 183

FREEDOM PAGES 185

THIS PLANNER BELONGS TO

_____

_____

_____

I'M SO PROUD OF YOU

WARNING

The use of this planner will change your life—if you let it. Change comes from awareness, which can be unfamiliar. There are some people who do not want awareness, regardless of the possibilities on the other side. Those people may not use planners. You are different. You want something different for your time, for your life, even if you do not know exactly what that is. There is hope available to you here. What would you do if you had all the time in the world? If you could slow down time, see it as it moves, and use all of it *exactly* the way you want to?

Everyone everywhere gets 24 hours in the day; it is the one equally distributed resource. CEOs, business tycoons, royalty, celebrities, politicians—they get the *same* 24 hours in a day that you do. What if you could access the same superpower of Time that they have? Regardless of your age, location, income, birthplace, or trauma—everyone everywhere gets 24 hours, until time stops for us. Until that very second, you still get 24 hours in the day.

This planner is different, in a wonderful, strange, and magical way, to support you in using *every moment* of the 24 hours gifted to you that you may have never even dreamed possible. Sound too good to be true? There is only one way to know for sure—to try it out for yourself. I invite you to investigate this planner and explore the new adventure and freedom that using it will bring. What do you have to lose?

REVOLUTION

I created this planner to stay on track throughout the day. Because of my ADHD, I would get lost in my own world.

Before this planner, it was a constant struggle that I was chronically late, everywhere. All my friends knew it. In a wedding party, I was even lied to about what time the wedding started so that I would be there on time. My spot in yoga was by the door because I was always the last one in. Driving would be in a panic that hopefully I could finish getting ready at stoplights and maybe if I speed then I will only be kind-of-late instead of really-late. I dropped out of grad school (for the 3rd time) because it did not feel like there were enough hours in the day to get everything done. My bosses would sit me down about my chronic tardiness and try to explain to me how to just arrive earlier, like I was an idiot. I am smart, and still could not seem to get there (or anywhere) on time. I even left a job that told me if I was ever late again, then I would be fired; I couldn't live in that constant fear because I knew it would happen again. I didn't have a reason for being late; I thought it was who I was. Time would get away from me. I over analyzed it; I went to time management seminars; I got prescriptions for ADHD medicine. Still nothing worked. I honestly tried my hardest to be somewhere on time, and still could not. Shame would chime in—"Why can't you be like other people and get there on time? What's wrong with you?"

I heard from some fellows about time recording. My initial reaction: "That's stupid," "What's the point?", and then "NO! I'M A FREE SPIRIT!" And though, I was miserable enough with the way things were to be curious about investigating something new. I'll try it out, I guess—begrudgingly.

I started looking around for time sheets that I could use. I found some that were detailed by the hour, although not as detailed as I wanted, and not for the hours I am awake. What if I get up at 4 am and I am in bed by 7 pm? What if I want to go to bed at 6 am and start my day at 2 pm? Everything that I could find out in the market assumed a 9 to 5 life, and they are not the boss of me. I started to create something that worked for me, looking ahead at the full 24 hours of the day. With this planner, I can be as detailed as every 5 minutes, or as big as hours at a time. So now I was writing down my time, which was helping, and there was something missing. I was still in complete vagueness about where I needed to be or when. So now I made a time planning sheet, that looked the same on a separate page. And then ADHD, I would completely forget to look at the planning sheet and get lost again. So now I combined them on the same sheet, with *the plan* on one side and *track data* on the other. I showed a friend. "*The* Plan? Eww—so much expectation already." Interesting; I do prefer gentleness to invite me out of the cave. So, I moved it to a *gentle* plan, and this planner was born.

I remember the first time that I used the planner and data tracking and actually arrived on time where I needed to be. Had I stumbled upon some strange time warp? What is going on? I used it again, and now I was not only on time, I arrived early. I had started to use the time in my day to get things done that I had not been able to find the time for. Could it be that simple? Like a good scientist, I tested my theory that I was cured of my time vagueness, stopped using the planner that day, and immediately was lost again, and again was arriving late. Okay so I am not cured, and I can access this superpower for daily (or hourly) freedom, in a partnership with Time. I can do that.

In addition to *me* using it every day, I started sharing my planner PDF with friends. People responded that it was helpful to stay on track throughout the day, as was my own experience. I took that as a sign from the Universe that the planner needed to be out in the world if it can help *other* people too, so I kept sharing the PDF, even with people I didn't really know that well. Over 400 people, and I kept getting the same response: "This is so helpful!" People would even send me pictures of their filled-out planner sheets. I am so grateful that what I created to help me can help others too. I also got some feedback I wasn't quite ready to hear—"Can you put it in a book? It's hard to carry around a piece of paper—Can you publish it?" Gulp. I clipped mine to a clipboard, which is fine at home, and is bulky and inconvenient to carry out into the world.

Fast forward to now. I have used this planner every day for three years, with only minimal tweaks to the design. Thanks to this planner, I went back to school and finished my MBA degree. I have learned there is only a 60-second window for being on-time, so typically I am early arriving places. Most importantly, I have used the planner to publish the planner, which is a chicken-egg scenario that I find to be a humorous gift of the Universe.

If I regularly check in with the planner, then I utilize my time. If I do not regularly check in with the planner, then my day gets away from me. The wonderful part is that at any point in the day I can begin again.

My purpose here is to share this planner with you and others worldwide so that you can spend your time in a way that serves you—to utilize all 24 hours you are given.

HOW DO I USE THIS PLANNER?

That's a great question. There is no perfect way.

I will share my experience of 3 years of using it, and then I invite you to play and be free—to experiment and investigate how it can work for you.

For me, the magic happens whenever I check-in with Time. When I take this willing action, I am able to steer my time in the direction I want to go in—how *I* want to use my time, in a way that serves me, instead of my time getting away from me.

You have permission to skip this section (or any section), skim the topics, or read it in any order. It is here for support if or when you could use some support. You also have permission to underline, circle, and draw notes all over this planner; it belongs to you and you can use it however you want.

TRACK DATA

I suggest starting with the tracking data side. When you notice the time, write down the time and what you're doing. That's it. I acknowledge what time it is by drawing a line at that time, and then writing above it what I was just doing. If I cannot remember what I did recently—gentleness—and I draw a squiggly line, or a made-up word, or words of encouragement, or draw a picture, or whatever you want. The noticing of the time is the progress, and progress IS perfection. When I notice the time or when I go to switch tasks, I check in with the planner and write it down, checking in with Time.

On the time tracking side, I use pen. That time has passed, and we grow from where we are. Gentleness. It is listed as data because I needed to see it as facts without bias. No shaming here. I find it most difficult to be honest with my time sheets, even though no one else sees them—it is difficult to be honest with myself about how I spent my time. My perfectionist creeps in about how I'm doing life wrong, so gentleness is key on this side. Recorded that I watched TV for 12 hours? That's wonderful—12 hours of time awareness is amazing progress! These time sheets are bonus points and not a weapon for self-harm. Gentleness... you're doing great!

If I wait until the end of the day to write down everything that I did all day, I do not find the magic here. Mostly because I cannot change the direction of the day. When I pause throughout the day for 30 seconds and write down what time it is and a one-or-few word summary of what I've done that I can remember, I am able to realign somehow. The hours used to sort of float by with me unaware of how to stop it. Pausing to record the time and what I'm doing pauses time and puts it on paper, so I can see it and realign.

The boxes can be broken down into 5-minute increments, and this encourages me to round time to the nearest 5 minutes. For example, if it is 8:37, I can round down to 8:35 or up to 8:40; dealer's choice. This rounding of time may sound silly, and I thought so initially, and it helps me be more aware of time. Magic here again that I cannot explain.

Sometimes a lot can happen in a 5-minute span. If I want a more detailed account of what happened, I will draw bubbles in the margins of what happened and arrows to when it happened.

GENTLE PLAN

For the gentle planning side, I use pencil. I get a giant eraser that I can erase and erase until my heart is content. I need to have the option to adjust to life as it is happening. It does not matter how committed I am to a certain activity or event, if I get a flat tire, I need to be able to adjust "the gentle plan" to exactly where I am in that moment. Using pencil reminds me that until that time has passed, I can change what I plan to do at any given moment.

This is the *gentle* plan, so gentleness on this side too. Some days I leave this side completely blank. Some days I only plan sleep and meals. I would caution against over-filling every moment of the day, especially initially. For me, when I plan every second of the entire day, I end up shutting down and hiding in my cave. Gentleness. Maybe plan one thing in each of the four columns of time.

I'M SO PROUD OF YOU FOR…

I added this to the planner to gently acknowledge things I did today that matter or were challenging, even if I am the only one who knows about it. Sometimes I will list these throughout the day, and sometimes fill it out at bedtime as I look over the day's events. Some days it is challenging to write even one; some days I like to write at least 3; some days I write many here and it is right-sized to be proud of you for all those big things.

Throughout the day when I hear the chatter of Shame, I am in the practice of balancing that with an "I'm proud of you for…" statement.

MINI ACTIONS FOR MINI GOALS

Shame will often chatter, THERE'S NO TIME FOR THAT! Go away, Shame. I'm proud of you for taking actions. In order to take the actions, I have different mini goals for different days. They are allowed to be different each day if I want to. Goals can be big "Life Goals" with a capital G or they can be mini goals, like community, sleep, or recovery. When I see that I did not get enough sleep for me to function, I add a sleep mini goal for the day, and mini actions for that are to put in my earplugs or put on my sleeping mask so that I can keep out the sights and sounds and take care of me with loving sleep. Maybe a mini goal for the day is community and an action I can take is to reach out to a fellow for support, smaller mini action before that is to pick up my phone, smaller mini action is to find my phone.

For a while I had "renew passport" as a box to check off for the day until I realized that renewing my passport is a mini goal and not a 5–15-minute action. The first action was research. I can investigate my next step when I am unsure of what it will be. What do I even need to do to renew my passport? Once I did a little bit of research online, one mini goal in the process is to fill out the paperwork, before that it is to print the paperwork, before that is to download the paperwork, before that is find the website, before that is open my web browser, before that is turn on my computer. So, the first action was really 'turn on computer', which is what I put on my planner for an action for the day—an action that I could accomplish. Eventually the end result of renewing my passport happened because all the mini actions along the way add up.

15 minutes a day is how this planner came to be. The idea of publishing my time sheets into a planner sounded so giant that I

could not fully dive into doing it initially. Where would I even start? Instead, I would commit to doing 15 minutes a day of research into publishing a planner and called it "publish research" so that I could fit those words into the 15-minute blocks. Some days it went well, and I would find out more information, and even go beyond the 15-minutes. Some days I would feel completely lost and overwhelmed. The ebb and flow like waves. Each day was the opportunity for something new. Keeping it in a 15-minute time commitment helped me stay aligned that it is "just research" and I am investigating for more information. Some days I would skip it (different days are allowed to have different mini goals) and naturally I would gravitate back to it. Eventually it got to the point where I had all the answers to the questions about getting started, and the rest of the questions I had would be answered in the process. We learn by doing. Once I decided to publish the planner and moved it from the back burner to my main focus, it took 8-weeks to publish, one day at a time. The miracle of this planner is that I was even able to do it at all.

Some days I am on fire and keep adding mini goals once I take the willing action for one, it gives Energy to taking more mini actions. I can do anything if it's in a 5-to-15-minute box. And though, what this also does sometimes is constantly moving the bar from me ever being able to celebrate the actions that I have taken. I invite you to investigate the balance here for what works for you.

5-MINUTES IS NOT ENOUGH! Go away, Shame. I'm proud of you for taking willing actions. 5-minutes is powerful for two reasons. The first is that it gives Energy to whatever it is I am doing. Energy multiplies and produces Energy somehow; 5-minutes of something self-caring and then I have Energy for that thing I have been putting off indefinitely. I have only stumbled upon this and do not know the why of why it works. I encourage you to test this theory for yourself.

The second is that time adds up. I created the chart below to show me how willing actions each day, even 5-minutes a day, add up to over 30 hours per year. Here is where Shame chimes in about the past and about "WASTED TIME!", and it is a practice to recognize it and respond—Go away, Shame. I'm proud of you for practicing time awareness. We grow from where we are. I now believe there is no such thing as 'wasted time' because it is constantly flowing, so it only needs a little redirection. A living amends to myself is that moving forward we will try this new path with gentleness. This chart is for encouragement that taking action *today* does make a difference. As long as I'm not dead, time keeps moving forward, and I have the opportunity to alter the path.

min per day	hours per month	hours per year
5	2.5	30.4
10	5.1	60.8
15	7.6	91.3
20	10.1	121.7
25	12.7	152.1
30	15.2	182.5
35	17.7	212.9
40	20.3	243.3
45	22.8	273.8
50	25.3	304.2
55	27.9	334.6
60	30.4	365.0

I CHANNEL THE ENERGY OF THE UNIVERSE!

The first action of the day may be to get out of bed. When the first action is difficult for whatever reason—that's okay, gentleness—I need something bigger than me to give me the Energy to take whatever that action is. Somewhere along the way I came up with saying, "I Channel the Energy of the Universe!" and I picture lightning striking or something powerful, loving, and bigger than me. I do not even need to define exactly what that is. I also raise my arms up and open up my hands when I say it, like the Universe is reaching down to hand me the Power of Lightning. "I Channel the Energy of the Universe!" and I picture some cartoon from my childhood where I can control Lightning. This practice seems to work every time (which is irritating some days and encouraging some days). When I raise my arms and say it—a physical action of surrender—it can simply mean that I tried and could use gentle support from whatever Power is out there. I am not even required to believe that it *will* work; it is a physical action where I am *acting as if* it will work. Some days it is, "I don't even think this will work, and (raise arms floppily) I Channel the Energy of the Universe or whatever." It still works anyway. If people are around me then I can say it in my head, and it looks like I am stretching; extra bonus points if I say it silly or with flair. "I Channel... the Energy... of the Universe!" I invite you to investigate this practice and see how it works for you. Also you are invited to look at the guided meditation in the back of this planner, as I started saying this around the time I wrote that.

I DO MY BEST AND I TAKE REST

If I were to explain how humans work to someone who did not know, I would explain sleep logically and with science about how it is necessary for humans to function, thrive, and brain. In the same breath I will also justify that in order to "get more done" today, I will restrict and withhold sleep—pretending that somehow this adds more hours in the day. Sleep deprivation is a torture technique. Let me say that again. Sleep deprivation is a torture technique. Shame says, "NO SLEEP AND NO FUN UNTIL EVERYTHING IS DONE!" Go away, Shame. I'm proud of you for sleeping.

I find that I am the best version of myself when I have had abundant sleep. And whatever my body says is abundant that day is perfect and complete; one day it is 14 hours and another day it is 6 hours. I cannot oversleep. I have tried sometimes to avoid the day altogether by wanting to sleep it away. And though, my body will only accept sleep until it no longer requires any more at this time, once my charger is at 100%. So if I am still able to sleep more, then my body needs more.

Say no to sleep-shame. My life does not typically align with the boxes of "8 hours sleep; 8 hours work; 8 hours other" that I have heard from others. There can be an embarrassment sometimes admitting that I slept 14 hours. It takes a gentle friend to remind me that my body needed it. I may be processing some trauma, stress, or am emotionally or physically drained in some way where my body's response to regroup and regenerate is sleep (which is its job). Allowing it to lead me on what I need is a practice and gentleness is important. The sleep-shame barometer goes all the way from "Why didn't you get more sleep?" to "Why are you sleeping so much?" and everything in between. There is no perfect amount of sleep to quiet the voice of Shame that wants to kick me endlessly. Go away, Shame. I'm proud of you for sleeping. It's a practice to convey the same gentleness with me that I would encourage with a friend. Have I accomplished enough to sleep? Sleep is not earned, it is a basic need; an investment into how the rest of the day will go.

Instead of writing the word 'sleep' for hours each day, I use a sleep symbol on the planner of a zig zag line so I can scan it and immediately see how much sleep I have gotten. I add up the hours I can see and the ones that roll over from the previous night. As you explore this, you may find that symbols for your planner reveal themselves to you.

I have found that if I do not give my body the sleep it needs at a time that is convenient to me, my body will eventually take the sleep it requires to function when it is inconvenient to me. This can range from sleeping past alarms to falling asleep at the wheel.

MULTI-TASKING

For me, there is no such thing as multi-tasking. The 5-minute boxes help keep me centered on one task at a time. When I am trying to multitask, I am still in vagueness about what it is I think I am accomplishing. Gentleness. Set the timer. Do one task, write down a one-or-few-word summary on the Track Data side, and then switch tasks, or continue what you are doing. No shaming here.

TIME HOSTAGES

There are other people out there who will want you to spend your time for them. They want me to share some of my 24 hours I have been given.

Could you look this up for me?

Hey watch this video.

Could you run this errand for me?

I want to ask you about something.

Can you work on this project for me?

In relationships with other people—family, friends, coworkers, acquaintances—sometimes there is give and take with regard to taking time from your day and doing something for someone else. I do volunteer work and service work all the time. I am not against that. However, there is this idea floating around that I cannot say no to service work requests, and today that idea no longer serves me. What I think is most important is doing it when I am in choice about it. Look at my planner—is this a convenient time *for me* to do it? I may be a yes for an activity and a no for at this time. That is okay. I am allowed to say no to other people when they ask for my time. I also do not need to give a full explanation about why I am saying no. No is a full sentence.

I can be in the middle of a task and am interrupted for something random and not urgent. I can say that I am not available right now to discuss this, and I do want to discuss it later. This sometimes involves setting boundaries with other people, or even with my phone.

My phone stays on do-not-disturb for certain hours of the day. My text messages do not have notifications; I plan for specific times of the day *that are convenient to me* to reach out and respond to messages. I can have a conversation with (adults that live in the house or coworkers nearby) about being interrupted. When interrupted—"Is this urgent? No? Let's talk on a break." Or, "I hear you. I am a yes for having this conversation, and a no for at-this-time."

URGENT! Other people's time urgency is not my responsibility. Sometimes people want an immediate response, and where that may be valid for brain surgery, in most instances it can wait. A practice I like to do is first acknowledge that I hear them, and then communicate that I will get back to them with an answer in—48 hours, 24 hours, by the end of the day, in an hour, in 10-minutes, or even one minute—all based on when a decision really needs to be made about it. Can it wait a day to pause? My favorite is 24-hours, as it gives me time to process what they are asking of me and the time to experience any emotions that may come up—before making a decision. I do all this to reconnect with Time, check in with me, look at my planner, and to pause for breath. What is most important for me here is to follow up with what I said on when I would get back to them, and I do that by writing it down on the daily planner to respond by the deadline.

I am allowed to change my mind. I may have committed to an event today, and now looking at how the day is going (triggers, sleep, illness, etc.), I would have never committed to it if asked right now. That usually means that I need to excuse myself from it, because it is the *gentle* plan and not the *rigid* plan. Is it life or death? Can I find a sub for it, reschedule it, or ask for support? Taking care of me is my number one priority.

DAILY JOURNALING

For quieting the brain chatter, it is a practice for me to journal 3 pages a day. I use that time to write down every thought that comes up, process through events, and separate out facts. I also use it to gently evaluate what is going on with my tracking data and ask Time for guidance—"Looks like I keep doing this here, and I'm stuck. Any ideas?" And then I keep writing and the ideas pop up later. The answers reveal themselves. I invite you to investigate this practice and see how it works for you.

Sometimes I can 'keep my own council', which can be great for getting to know me, and not great if something is a little out there. Just to double check the actions[1] I am getting direction on are from my True Self, are they aligned with my integrity and values? Are they aligned with the spiritual text that I read from (if any)? A second way to double check is to bounce the ideas off someone safe because "more light comes in through two windows than one."[2] What is crucial here is that this person I choose to share my visions with won't drain my Spirit or stomp on my dreams—someone else who truly has my best interest at heart and wants to see me shine *without it being a threat to them*. It is also okay if that person is not a family member or romantic partner.

I will purge all the thoughts on paper to help me quiet the chatter, and I am allowed to divide up my journaling throughout the day— when I wake up, during the day, and especially when I am almost ready for bed (when my body is tired, and my brain is not). I used to think I had to finish it all at one time, or specifically at one time of the day, and that idea no longer serves me today. One thing this planner has taught me is that whatever I want to do with my time— I can divide it up throughout the day and it all adds up the same.

I often want to debate what is possible versus what is probable. For some things I make a T-chart because I need to see it all on paper—to look at the facts and feelings. Your feelings are valid. I made a T-chart when I was considering publishing this planner. I find it helpful to play out all scenarios on paper instead of letting them

---

[1] Author John E. Batterson
[2] Author John E. Batterson

float around in vagueness in my head. Negative side: This side comes naturally to me for whatever reason. What if it doesn't work out? For me, Fear usually says, CHANGE—BAD! Counter thoughts, positive side—This side is a practice for me. Often times I have no idea how to come up with this side. Gentleness. How would I encourage a friend and hold space for them? Sometimes just acting as if it is possible can help get me out of the cave. Not in a 'toxic positivity' sort of way, in an is-it-even-possible sort of way. Do I dare to dream?

-	+
Shame says...	Hope says...
Fear says...	Gentleness says...
Panic! Panic! says...	Encouragement says...
Worst Possible Outcome...	Best Possible Outcome...

MAX TIMES

Certain activities have a max time that I can do them before I start to naturally switch to other things. When that comes up, I find it important to listen and sometimes negotiate, depending on the circumstances. Sometimes it is that I do not want to forget to do this other thing, so Time keeps reminding me, so I write it down in the gentle planner and go back to what I was doing. Other times it is Time signaling that we are done, and the Drill Sergeant won't let go and says YOU CANNOT STOP. Again, the practice of listening and checking in with myself. Is this a gentle Time nudge or the Drill Sergeant bully?

Creative projects that I want to be in the flow, I allow that when I have time in my day for it. I can create or do whatever I want until this time, and then I will switch to this other thing. That is the flexibility that I find with this planner. My free Spirit gets to create in a way that serves me, and I can take a break every 3-to-6-hours for bathroom, water, and food. Activities have different max times—where forcing myself to continue when I am miserable at that point only results in diminished returns. For me, I could only study for one hour or so for school and then needed to do something else, and then go back to studying, if I want. (Even a 5-minute break to throw in a load of laundry or have a 5-minute dance party.) Other things have a much shorter shelf life, for example I can only do dishes for 15 minutes and then I am done, and I can come back to it again later. I invite you to investigate your time limits for certain activities, in a way that is gentle and suits you.

The old me was afraid of losing momentum, because if I stopped something then I would typically never go back to it. Now I know that if I write it down on the daily and weekly gentle plan, then I will go back to it again.

GENTLE TIME HONESTY

I find it to be a practice of awareness that triggers can still get me off-balance and time-vague again. As I learn through experience what those triggers are and come back to my planner and check in with Time, the duration is shorter, and gentleness that it can still happen. Also, awareness that I have been in time-vagueness my whole life and it is still a new thing for me to be time-aware, and progress IS perfection.

Another practice that I began into using my planner is stop identifying as late and stopped saying 'I am late'. Late is no longer my identity, and there is something strangely powerful about using the I AM statement. When I would say 'I am late' it was a shame-hit, made me feel less-than, and would distract me for the duration of whatever event I was there for. I started changing it to 'I have arrived later than initially anticipated' or 'I arrived after the meeting started' and finding the gentleness in just-the-facts.

I also have stopped apologizing for arriving later than anticipated. This may sound weird or rude, and I find it to be a loving practice to me. I find the direct approach to be one that quiets the voice of Shame, rather than pretending it did not happen and letting it hover awkwardly. Go away, Shame. I'm proud of you for practicing time-honesty. I will separate out the facts. My Maps app has the option to share arrival time with people so I will use that as well to be time-honest. Or say, "I arrived later than I initially agreed to. I value you, your time, and our relationship. My arriving late has nothing to do with you." I know that is bold to say, so sometimes a direct approach may not be best, depending on the circumstance. I can still think it, though. My arriving late has nothing to do with other people and only to do with me and my relationship with Time.

My relationship with Time is a practice, and I can investigate my data tracking later and find gentleness for myself that it is not a perfect-practice, it is a progress-practice. Sometimes it happened because a trigger got my whole day off balance. Sometimes it happened because I was not yet accurate with how long some things take me. Sometimes it happened because I had it on my plan to start getting ready at the time I needed to, and then I did not look at the planner. Gentleness and investigation.

ALARMS

Once I have my gentle plan for what the day looks like, I set alarms on my phone to go off when I need to switch to the next activity. Often times an alarm goes off and I am in complete vagueness about what it's for. Gentleness, that's okay. Then I practice looking at the planner to find out what it is for. Also, sometimes I have a trauma response to alarms blaring, so it is okay to experiment and explore options that are gentle for you.

This planner only works if I actually look at it. My alarms only work to alert me if I can hear them to remind me to look at the planner. Gentleness that some days I may hide from the planner and from my phone to hear alarms. Time-awareness is a gentle practice that I can jump back into again when I am ready.

I am allowed to not use the planner all the time. Some people use the planner for only during-work-hours, some use it for any-hours-not-at-work. Some use it only-on-weekends, others for only-on-weekdays. Gentleness that in whatever way you want to use this planner is perfect and complete.

What about when I cannot look at the planner? I find it grounding to look at the time, and when I cannot have the planner in front of me, there are other options. While driving, I use Maps with audible directions. Other times I will find a scrap of paper and use time awareness to write down the time and what I'm doing and add it to the planner later (if I want to). I will also sometimes take a picture which typically records the time and what I'm doing. Also gentleness that the planner is there to support me and not drown me, so I am allowed to take a break from it for as long as I want, and come back to it if or when I'm ready to.

WHAT DO YOU NEED RIGHT MEOW?

No idea. Am I sleepy or hungry? No idea. For me, coffee and energy drinks are not actually a substitute for sleep or fuel. I am in the practice of learning what my body needs. I will drink a large glass of water; and if I am actually hungry, then I get really hungry. Can I take a 15-minute power nap (close my eyes and be still) instead of looking for a pick me up? What does my body even need? I adapted HALT (that I'd heard from others) into something that addressed more of me. When I am in complete vagueness about what I need— gentleness—and I just go down this list for a gentle inventory of where I am at. I investigate what my body needs right now and explore—how can I take care of me? Have I done anything fun today? What can I add to align towards a balanced life? Do I need to go to the bathroom? Have I showered today? Gentleness. Can I be in movement where my body is in motion and my brain is free (for example, exercise, gardening, shower, etc.)?

M	Menstrual	Menstrual accessment, lovingly, of where in cycle and how that affects the day. This may apply to you directly or indirectly.
H	Hungry	Eat1, Eat2, Eat3, Snack1, Snack2. Water all day.
A	Angry	Typically comes out for me when my boundaries are violated. Journaling helps. Or movement.
L	Lonely	Is there someone safe I can reach out to for friendship and fellowship?
T	Tired	What level am I operating at? How can I add abundant sleep? Rest can be to close my eyes and be still.
T	Trigger	I draw giant *** on planner for triggers because I will have trigger amnesia later when I'm squirrelly
S	Squirrelly	For when I am feeling something and I have no idea what
S	Spiritual	How can I re-align and re-center with my True Self or Higher Power? What helps me feel grounded?
S	Sunlight	Daily Sunlight Rx. Can I get outside for a few minutes? Even if it's cold or rainy and get natural light? Smell some outside air and realign?

I came up with DANAA as a code for my planner to describe certain moments, interactions, or triggers.

D	Dysfunction
A	Addiction
N	Neglect
A	Abuse
A	Abandonment

I have noticed that when I shrug and say, "It's fine" that I feel a little smaller and want to hide back in my cave. I came up with an acronym for FINE that reminds me that it is an invitation to shine. Now when I hear myself say, "It's fine", then I am challenged to stand up for me and do the opposite of what I was just giving up on. If I find it challenging, that is bonus fun.

F	First
I	Indicator of
N	Neglected
E	Empowerment

I did not create this one for SHAME and have heard it from others, and I still find it to be powerful, so I am sharing it here.

S	Should
H	Have
A	Already
M	Mastered
E	Everything

AFTER TIME, MORE DETAILED

After some experience with the gentle planning side, the most detailed I will get with planning is the 15-minute blocks. If I have the whole day available (minus sleep and meals), the most I will put on the planner is something at the top of the hour for 15-minutes, as options available. I also have permission to do them in any order and skip around. I invite you to experiment and investigate what works for you. Certain things have a home they like at certain times of the day.

I will split the gentle plan boxes in half, too, if I want to. At this time, I may want to journal or take a prosperous nap. It is the gentle plan, and I can decide at the time if I want to do the options I wrote down or do something different.

My gentle plan has things that are a **yes-yes**: yes for this time and a yes for the activity, and then other things that are **maybe-yes**: flexible for this time (maybe today or tomorrow) and a yes for this activity. I draw symbols in the time boxes to signal the yes-yes items—for example an asterisk*, heart, or circle—so that visually I can glance at my planner and see where the yes-yes's are. Okay I have a call at 6 o'clock and plans at 8 o'clock, so I will signal those, and then I know the rest of the day's gentle plans are flexible.

My perfectionist sometimes goes insane when the boxes do not line up between the gentle plan and track data sides (YOU SAID YOU WOULD EAT AT 5:00 AND YOU ATE AT 5:30! PANIC! PANIC!)—Go away, Shame. We practice gentleness. I'm proud of you for eating. This is an alignment and a practice. I can do whatever I want, and no one is the boss of me.

UNIVERSE-SUPPORTED

I add support to my daily planner because I need to see it and read it daily; a reminder that I am supported by the Universe. Here are some that I came up with that help me; add your own as they reveal themselves to you. Sometimes when I say some of them, I put my hand on my heart and tap gently. Some of these are to me and some are a practice of what I say to others.

A list here (or anywhere) does not help me until I have moved it to the daily planner where I will actually see it.

Gentleness

It's Okay; You're Okay; You're Doing Great

I'm So Proud of You

If I Find It Challenging, That Is Bonus Fun

We Grow from Where We Are

It's Okay to Be Big in the World and Shine

If You Can Do It, I Can Do It

Time Takes Time

Your Feelings Are Valid

I Practice Speaking My Truth

Self-Caring is Not Selfish

We Work with What We've Got

The Answers Reveal Themselves

I Love You Forever, No Matter What

Different Days Are Allowed to Have Different Mini Goals

You're Exactly Where You're Supposed to Be Right Now

I Channel the Energy of the Universe

We Celebrate Progress Here

It's Okay to Cry. There Is Nothing Wrong with Crying.

We Learn by Doing

You Need My Permission to Touch Me

I Take the Daily Willing Action and Surrender the Results[3]

Progress IS Perfection

I Practice Asking for What I Want, Even If   on't Get It

Gentleness For My Past Self—(circle yours,   ou want to):
They Were Doing the Best They   d
She Was Doing the Best She C
He Was Doing the Best He Co

Loving Boundaries Are Self-Caring to Me

---

[3] Have heard some version of this from others

It's Okay to Play and Be Free

I Do My Best and I Take Rest

It's Okay... It'll Work Out

Flower Buds Have Been Growing Long Before They Bloom

Do I Dare to Dream?

Any Time Awareness Is Bonus Points and Not Weapons For Self-Harm

WIDER GENTLE PLAN: 6-WEEKS

I used to look at planners-by-the-month with such vagueness around time and space. Something due on the 1st of next month? That's so far away! Nope—it's two days away.

I created this wider gentle plan for 6-weeks so that I can see the days as they actually are—next to each other.

6-weeks for this planner, and (optional) the 6-weeks that follow this planner.

YEAR/ MONTHS: _____

GENTLE PLAN							GENTLE PLAN							GENTLE PLAN							GENTLE PLAN						
Mo	Tu	We	Th	Fr	Sa	Su	Mo	Tu	We	Th	Fr	Sa	Su	Mo	Tu	We	Th	Fr	Sa	Su	Mo	Tu	We	Th	Fr	Sa	Su

I'M SO PROUD OF YOU

GENTLE PLAN	GENTLE PLAN	GENTLE PLAN	GENTLE PLAN
Mo Tu We Th Fr Sa Su	Mo Tu We Th Fr Sa Su	Mo Tu We Th Fr Sa Su	REPEAT
			RANDOM

YEAR/ MONTHS: _____

GENTLE PLAN	GENTLE PLAN	GENTLE PLAN	GENTLE PLAN
Mo Tu We Th Fr Sa Su	Mo Tu We Th Fr Sa Su	Mo Tu We Th Fr Sa Su	Mo Tu We Th Fr Sa Su

I'M SO PROUD OF YOU

GENTLE PLAN	GENTLE PLAN	GENTLE PLAN	GENTLE PLAN
Mo Tu We Th Fr Sa Su	Mo Tu We Th Fr Sa Su	Mo Tu We Th Fr Sa Su	REPEAT
			RANDOM

GENTLE WEEK PLANNING: REMEMBER BOXES

I started these boxes instead of a weekly to-do list. Visually lines of lists blurred together for me, so the separated boxes help me to see each item individually. I will also use this as a do-not-forget list, formerly things I would write on my hand. The key factor that decides whether movement happens on these items is

    A) Turning them into 5-to-15-minute actions, and

    B) Writing them on my daily planner.

To find a gentle home on the gentle plan.

A list here (or anywhere) does not help me until I have moved it to the daily planner where I will actually see it.

These boxes work the other direction as well. I will take things I had on today's gentle plan that didn't get done and move them here so I will not forget them, and also possibly so I can break them down into smaller mini actions before adding them to the next day's gentle plan.

Some options are—homework assignments, business deadlines, or drawing tiny pictures. Other options are—random ideas that pop up, encouraging words, or investigation list. More options are—career, vision work, furbabies, pets, human babies, medical, etc.

This space is for whatever you need, and you do not need to decide right now.

I tried pencil here at first, and then I erased them all and could never see the progress or all the actions I took. Now I use pen here and cross out the items that need to be smaller and check off ones that I have done. I have noticed that when things stay on the list for a while, it is because what is listed is not actually the next step towards a mini goal. Can I break it down into a smaller 5-to-15-minute action? Or even a one-minute action? The actions to get something done outside of the house are to leave the house, and before that get dressed, and before that shower (optional), and before that get out of bed. So, the first action is to get out of bed.

Mini action for dishes is put my hands under the water; before that turn on the sink water; before that is go to the sink. Also, I don't have to do the dishes. I don't have to do anything. If I want to, I will go over to the sink. I commit to nothing beyond going over to the sink.

There are enough pages here for 6-weeks, and though, my experience is that some rollover to the following week.

One of my favorite things is to have a "That's Stupid" list. I have a lot of ideas pop into my head, and my natural response is often to flick them away with, "That's Stupid" or "What's the Point?" I made a commitment when I started this planner that I would write down the ideas that came about, and only later would I decide if they were, in fact, stupid. This planner was one of those ideas, as are many of my other projects that bring me joy. I invite you to experiment with this if you'd like to. My inner Muse is often tapping at what would bring me joy.

Topic: NO * MAYBE * YES: _____

GENTLE PLAN	GENTLE PLAN	GENTLE PLAN	GENTLE PLAN

Topic: NO * MAYBE * YES: _____

GENTLE PLAN	GENTLE PLAN	GENTLE PLAN	GENTLE PLAN

Topic: NO * MAYBE * YES: _____

GENTLE PLAN	GENTLE PLAN	GENTLE PLAN	GENTLE PLAN

Topic: NO * MAYBE * YES: _____

GENTLE PLAN	GENTLE PLAN	GENTLE PLAN	GENTLE PLAN

Topic: NO * MAYBE * YES: _____

GENTLE PLAN	GENTLE PLAN	GENTLE PLAN	GENTLE PLAN

Topic: NO * MAYBE * YES: _____

GENTLE PLAN	GENTLE PLAN	GENTLE PLAN	GENTLE PLAN

Topic: NO * MAYBE * YES: _____

GENTLE PLAN	GENTLE PLAN	GENTLE PLAN	GENTLE PLAN

Topic: NO * MAYBE * YES: _____

GENTLE PLAN	GENTLE PLAN	GENTLE PLAN	GENTLE PLAN

Topic: NO * MAYBE * YES: _____

GENTLE PLAN	GENTLE PLAN	GENTLE PLAN	GENTLE PLAN

Topic: NO * MAYBE * YES: _____

GENTLE PLAN	GENTLE PLAN	GENTLE PLAN	GENTLE PLAN

Topic: NO * MAYBE * YES: _____

GENTLE PLAN	GENTLE PLAN	GENTLE PLAN	GENTLE PLAN

Topic: NO * MAYBE * YES: _____

GENTLE PLAN	GENTLE PLAN	GENTLE PLAN	GENTLE PLAN

GENTLE WEEK 1

Congratulations on starting this new journey. All your feelings are valid. Wonder and Excitement and Curiosity and Nervous and all the feelings are welcome here—come in and have a seat on the couch—we will start this journey together. I'm so proud of you for trying something new. Even if this is not your first time using this planner, this is a new 6-weeks, and I am still proud of you for trying something new again.

This week is where you will begin the data collection. Not judging; you are an impartial observer. We practice being an investigator for how long things take, with gentleness. When I notice the time, draw a line at that time and write above it what I was just doing, if I can remember. Gentleness.

More options here, if you'd like. How long does it take to shower on the days you do? No idea. I learn this by writing down when I start and again when I'm done. How long does it take to arrive at your regular destination? No idea. I learn this by writing down when I leave and again when I have arrived at the place and in my spot of where I need to be. How much sleep did you get? No idea. I learn this by writing down when I start my routine of winding down for bed, and then write down again when I wake up. It's a practice, and sometimes I forget to write down when I start something or when I finish. Gentleness. I can write down when I notice the time and what I'm doing. Be your own private investigator this week, with gentleness as a casual observer. A gentle and honest inventory of where we are; we grow from where we are.

When Shame starts to chime in, "It took you that long to get ready? FAIL!" I protect me—Go away, Shame. I'm proud of you for getting ready.

Country of the Day: I Channel the Energy of the Universe!

	GENTLE PLAN	TRACK DATA		GENTLE PLAN	TRACK DATA
12 00 AM			06 00 AM		
12 15			06 15		
12 30			06 30		
12 45			06 45		
01 00 AM			07 00 AM		
01 15			07 15		
01 30			07 30		
01 45			07 45		
02 00 AM			08 00 AM		
02 15			08 15		
02 30			08 30		
02 45			08 45		
03 00 AM			09 00 AM		
03 15			09 15		
03 30			09 30		
03 45			09 45		
04 00 AM			10 00 AM		
04 15			10 15		
04 30			10 30		
04 45			10 45		
05 00 AM			11 00 AM		
05 15			11 15		
05 30			11 30		
05 45			11 45		

mini goals --> mini actions 5 - 15 min

DATE: DAY: Mo   Tu   We   Th   Fr   Sa   Su

	GENTLE PLAN	TRACK DATA		GENTLE PLAN	TRACK DATA
12 00 PM			06 00 PM		
12 15			06 15		
12 30			06 30		
12 45			06 45		
01 00 PM			07 00 PM		
01 15			07 15		
01 30			07 30		
01 45			07 45		
02 00 PM			08 00 PM		
02 15			08 15		
02 30			08 30		
02 45			08 45		
03 00 PM			09 00 PM		
03 15			09 15		
03 30			09 30		
03 45			09 45		
04 00 PM			10 00 PM		
04 15			10 15		
04 30			10 30		
04 45			10 45		
05 00 PM			11 00 PM		
05 15			11 15		
05 30			11 30		
05 45			11 45		

I'm so proud of you for...

Country of the Day: I Channel the Energy of the Universe!

	GENTLE PLAN	TRACK DATA		GENTLE PLAN	TRACK DATA
12 00 AM			06 00 AM		
12 15			06 15		
12 30			06 30		
12 45			06 45		
01 00 AM			07 00 AM		
01 15			07 15		
01 30			07 30		
01 45			07 45		
02 00 AM			08 00 AM		
02 15			08 15		
02 30			08 30		
02 45			08 45		
03 00 AM			09 00 AM		
03 15			09 15		
03 30			09 30		
03 45			09 45		
04 00 AM			10 00 AM		
04 15			10 15		
04 30			10 30		
04 45			10 45		
05 00 AM			11 00 AM		
05 15			11 15		
05 30			11 30		
05 45			11 45		

mini goals --> mini actions 5 - 15 min

DATE: DAY: Mo Tu We Th Fr Sa Su

	GENTLE PLAN	TRACK DATA		GENTLE PLAN	TRACK DATA
12 00 PM			06 00 PM		
12 15			06 15		
12 30			06 30		
12 45			06 45		
01 00 PM			07 00 PM		
01 15			07 15		
01 30			07 30		
01 45			07 45		
02 00 PM			08 00 PM		
02 15			08 15		
02 30			08 30		
02 45			08 45		
03 00 PM			09 00 PM		
03 15			09 15		
03 30			09 30		
03 45			09 45		
04 00 PM			10 00 PM		
04 15			10 15		
04 30			10 30		
04 45			10 45		
05 00 PM			11 00 PM		
05 15			11 15		
05 30			11 30		
05 45			11 45		

I'm so proud of you for...

Country of the Day: I Channel the Energy of the Universe!

	GENTLE PLAN	TRACK DATA		GENTLE PLAN	TRACK DATA
12 00 AM			06 00 AM		
12 15			06 15		
12 30			06 30		
12 45			06 45		
01 00 AM			07 00 AM		
01 15			07 15		
01 30			07 30		
01 45			07 45		
02 00 AM			08 00 AM		
02 15			08 15		
02 30			08 30		
02 45			08 45		
03 00 AM			09 00 AM		
03 15			09 15		
03 30			09 30		
03 45			09 45		
04 00 AM			10 00 AM		
04 15			10 15		
04 30			10 30		
04 45			10 45		
05 00 AM			11 00 AM		
05 15			11 15		
05 30			11 30		
05 45			11 45		

mini goals --> mini actions 5 - 15 min

DATE: DAY: Mo Tu We Th Fr Sa Su

GENTLE PLAN	TRACK DATA		GENTLE PLAN	TRACK DATA
12 00 PM		06 00 PM		
12 15		06 15		
12 30		06 30		
12 45		06 45		
01 00 PM		07 00 PM		
01 15		07 15		
01 30		07 30		
01 45		07 45		
02 00 PM		08 00 PM		
02 15		08 15		
02 30		08 30		
02 45		08 45		
03 00 PM		09 00 PM		
03 15		09 15		
03 30		09 30		
03 45		09 45		
04 00 PM		10 00 PM		
04 15		10 15		
04 30		10 30		
04 45		10 45		
05 00 PM		11 00 PM		
05 15		11 15		
05 30		11 30		
05 45		11 45		

I'm so proud of you for...

Country of the Day: I Channel the Energy of the Universe!

	GENTLE PLAN	TRACK DATA		GENTLE PLAN	TRACK DATA
12 00 AM			06 00 AM		
12 15			06 15		
12 30			06 30		
12 45			06 45		
01 00 AM			07 00 AM		
01 15			07 15		
01 30			07 30		
01 45			07 45		
02 00 AM			08 00 AM		
02 15			08 15		
02 30			08 30		
02 45			08 45		
03 00 AM			09 00 AM		
03 15			09 15		
03 30			09 30		
03 45			09 45		
04 00 AM			10 00 AM		
04 15			10 15		
04 30			10 30		
04 45			10 45		
05 00 AM			11 00 AM		
05 15			11 15		
05 30			11 30		
05 45			11 45		

mini goals --> mini actions 5 - 15 min

DATE: _____   DAY: Mo Tu We Th Fr Sa Su

	GENTLE PLAN	TRACK DATA		GENTLE PLAN	TRACK DATA
12 00 PM			06 00 PM		
12 15			06 15		
12 30			06 30		
12 45			06 45		
01 00 PM			07 00 PM		
01 15			07 15		
01 30			07 30		
01 45			07 45		
02 00 PM			08 00 PM		
02 15			08 15		
02 30			08 30		
02 45			08 45		
03 00 PM			09 00 PM		
03 15			09 15		
03 30			09 30		
03 45			09 45		
04 00 PM			10 00 PM		
04 15			10 15		
04 30			10 30		
04 45			10 45		
05 00 PM			11 00 PM		
05 15			11 15		
05 30			11 30		
05 45			11 45		

I'm so proud of you for...

Country of the Day: I Channel the Energy of the Universe!

	GENTLE PLAN	TRACK DATA		GENTLE PLAN	TRACK DATA
12 00 AM			06 00 AM		
12 15			06 15		
12 30			06 30		
12 45			06 45		
01 00 AM			07 00 AM		
01 15			07 15		
01 30			07 30		
01 45			07 45		
02 00 AM			08 00 AM		
02 15			08 15		
02 30			08 30		
02 45			08 45		
03 00 AM			09 00 AM		
03 15			09 15		
03 30			09 30		
03 45			09 45		
04 00 AM			10 00 AM		
04 15			10 15		
04 30			10 30		
04 45			10 45		
05 00 AM			11 00 AM		
05 15			11 15		
05 30			11 30		
05 45			11 45		

mini goals --> mini actions 5 - 15 min

DATE: _____ DAY: Mo Tu We Th Fr Sa Su

	GENTLE PLAN	TRACK DATA		GENTLE PLAN	TRACK DATA
12 00 PM			06 00 PM		
12 15			06 15		
12 30			06 30		
12 45			06 45		
01 00 PM			07 00 PM		
01 15			07 15		
01 30			07 30		
01 45			07 45		
02 00 PM			08 00 PM		
02 15			08 15		
02 30			08 30		
02 45			08 45		
03 00 PM			09 00 PM		
03 15			09 15		
03 30			09 30		
03 45			09 45		
04 00 PM			10 00 PM		
04 15			10 15		
04 30			10 30		
04 45			10 45		
05 00 PM			11 00 PM		
05 15			11 15		
05 30			11 30		
05 45			11 45		

I'm so proud of you for...

Country of the Day: I Channel the Energy of the Universe!

	GENTLE PLAN	TRACK DATA		GENTLE PLAN	TRACK DATA
12 00 AM			06 00 AM		
12 15			06 15		
12 30			06 30		
12 45			06 45		
01 00 AM			07 00 AM		
01 15			07 15		
01 30			07 30		
01 45			07 45		
02 00 AM			08 00 AM		
02 15			08 15		
02 30			08 30		
02 45			08 45		
03 00 AM			09 00 AM		
03 15			09 15		
03 30			09 30		
03 45			09 45		
04 00 AM			10 00 AM		
04 15			10 15		
04 30			10 30		
04 45			10 45		
05 00 AM			11 00 AM		
05 15			11 15		
05 30			11 30		
05 45			11 45		

mini goals --> mini actions 5 - 15 min

DATE: DAY: Mo Tu We Th Fr Sa Su

	GENTLE PLAN	TRACK DATA		GENTLE PLAN	TRACK DATA
12 00 PM			06 00 PM		
12 15			06 15		
12 30			06 30		
12 45			06 45		
01 00 PM			07 00 PM		
01 15			07 15		
01 30			07 30		
01 45			07 45		
02 00 PM			08 00 PM		
02 15			08 15		
02 30			08 30		
02 45			08 45		
03 00 PM			09 00 PM		
03 15			09 15		
03 30			09 30		
03 45			09 45		
04 00 PM			10 00 PM		
04 15			10 15		
04 30			10 30		
04 45			10 45		
05 00 PM			11 00 PM		
05 15			11 15		
05 30			11 30		
05 45			11 45		

I'm so proud of you for...

Country of the Day: I Channel the Energy of the Universe!

	GENTLE PLAN	TRACK DATA		GENTLE PLAN	TRACK DATA
12 00 AM			06 00 AM		
12 15			06 15		
12 30			06 30		
12 45			06 45		
01 00 AM			07 00 AM		
01 15			07 15		
01 30			07 30		
01 45			07 45		
02 00 AM			08 00 AM		
02 15			08 15		
02 30			08 30		
02 45			08 45		
03 00 AM			09 00 AM		
03 15			09 15		
03 30			09 30		
03 45			09 45		
04 00 AM			10 00 AM		
04 15			10 15		
04 30			10 30		
04 45			10 45		
05 00 AM			11 00 AM		
05 15			11 15		
05 30			11 30		
05 45			11 45		

mini goals --> mini actions 5 - 15 min

DATE: DAY: Mo   Tu   We   Th   Fr   Sa   Su

	GENTLE PLAN	TRACK DATA		GENTLE PLAN	TRACK DATA
12 00 PM			06 00 PM		
12 15			06 15		
12 30			06 30		
12 45			06 45		
01 00 PM			07 00 PM		
01 15			07 15		
01 30			07 30		
01 45			07 45		
02 00 PM			08 00 PM		
02 15			08 15		
02 30			08 30		
02 45			08 45		
03 00 PM			09 00 PM		
03 15			09 15		
03 30			09 30		
03 45			09 45		
04 00 PM			10 00 PM		
04 15			10 15		
04 30			10 30		
04 45			10 45		
05 00 PM			11 00 PM		
05 15			11 15		
05 30			11 30		
05 45			11 45		

I'm so proud of you for...

GENTLE WEEK 2

Can you believe you have already made it to Week 2? Wonderful! I'm so proud of you!

You have the option to continue the way in which you used this planner in Week One with gentle observations, if you prefer.

Another option is to gently look at your experience with the tracking side of the planner for some data collection. Gentleness. This is a practice. It is okay to have large chunks of unaccounted time. There is still progress here, and Progress IS Perfection. *Any* time awareness you have had this past week is bonus points, not weapons for self-harm. You're doing great. I'm so proud of you.

Now you have some data. Gentle information to be a gentle guide for the gentle planning. How long did it take to shower on the days you did? Gentle plan for that this week. How long did it take to arrive at your regular destination? Gentle plan for that this week. How about your sleep—did you feel rested? "Oh looks like I typically slept __ hours." Was I still tired on that amount of sleep? Can I plan for more? I.e., I notice that I do ___ at this time, and maybe I could try ___ for 15 minutes instead.

Didn't record how long some things took? Gentleness.

Being a gentle observer and then a scientist with experiments. "Interesting, I seem to do *this* here, maybe this week I will try *that* instead and see how it goes." I find that a gentleness and playfulness while experimenting can be the most helpful. Say no to Shame and no to the Drill Sergeant that says everything must be done perfectly. We are perfectly imperfect and this is an alignment. We are impartial observers of data facts. We can practice alignment towards the direction we want to go in.

Keep doing what you're doing. Practice your balance and alignment in the ebb and flow between the data tracking and gentle planning. Gentleness. Investigation. Read and re-read the 'How Do I Use This Planner?' and 'Universe-Supported' sections as many times as are helpful. Have you skipped ahead to the 'Country of the Day' and 'Guided Meditation'? It's okay to skip around this planner as much as you want. Enjoy. You're doing great. I'm so proud of you.

Country of the Day: I Channel the Energy of the Universe!

	GENTLE PLAN	TRACK DATA		GENTLE PLAN	TRACK DATA
12 00 AM			06 00 AM		
12 15			06 15		
12 30			06 30		
12 45			06 45		
01 00 AM			07 00 AM		
01 15			07 15		
01 30			07 30		
01 45			07 45		
02 00 AM			08 00 AM		
02 15			08 15		
02 30			08 30		
02 45			08 45		
03 00 AM			09 00 AM		
03 15			09 15		
03 30			09 30		
03 45			09 45		
04 00 AM			10 00 AM		
04 15			10 15		
04 30			10 30		
04 45			10 45		
05 00 AM			11 00 AM		
05 15			11 15		
05 30			11 30		
05 45			11 45		

mini goals --> mini actions 5 - 15 min

DATE: DAY: Mo   Tu   We   Th   Fr   Sa   Su

	GENTLE PLAN	TRACK DATA		GENTLE PLAN	TRACK DATA
12 00 PM			06 00 PM		
12 15			06 15		
12 30			06 30		
12 45			06 45		
01 00 PM			07 00 PM		
01 15			07 15		
01 30			07 30		
01 45			07 45		
02 00 PM			08 00 PM		
02 15			08 15		
02 30			08 30		
02 45			08 45		
03 00 PM			09 00 PM		
03 15			09 15		
03 30			09 30		
03 45			09 45		
04 00 PM			10 00 PM		
04 15			10 15		
04 30			10 30		
04 45			10 45		
05 00 PM			11 00 PM		
05 15			11 15		
05 30			11 30		
05 45			11 45		

I'm so proud of you for...

Country of the Day: I Channel the Energy of the Universe!

	GENTLE PLAN	TRACK DATA		GENTLE PLAN	TRACK DATA
12 00 AM			06 00 AM		
12 15			06 15		
12 30			06 30		
12 45			06 45		
01 00 AM			07 00 AM		
01 15			07 15		
01 30			07 30		
01 45			07 45		
02 00 AM			08 00 AM		
02 15			08 15		
02 30			08 30		
02 45			08 45		
03 00 AM			09 00 AM		
03 15			09 15		
03 30			09 30		
03 45			09 45		
04 00 AM			10 00 AM		
04 15			10 15		
04 30			10 30		
04 45			10 45		
05 00 AM			11 00 AM		
05 15			11 15		
05 30			11 30		
05 45			11 45		

mini goals --> mini actions 5 - 15 min

DATE: DAY: Mo Tu We Th Fr Sa Su

	GENTLE PLAN	TRACK DATA		GENTLE PLAN	TRACK DATA
12 00 PM			06 00 PM		
12 15			06 15		
12 30			06 30		
12 45			06 45		
01 00 PM			07 00 PM		
01 15			07 15		
01 30			07 30		
01 45			07 45		
02 00 PM			08 00 PM		
02 15			08 15		
02 30			08 30		
02 45			08 45		
03 00 PM			09 00 PM		
03 15			09 15		
03 30			09 30		
03 45			09 45		
04 00 PM			10 00 PM		
04 15			10 15		
04 30			10 30		
04 45			10 45		
05 00 PM			11 00 PM		
05 15			11 15		
05 30			11 30		
05 45			11 45		

I'm so proud of you for...

Country of the Day: I Channel the Energy of the Universe!

	GENTLE PLAN	TRACK DATA		GENTLE PLAN	TRACK DATA
12 00 AM			06 00 AM		
12 15			06 15		
12 30			06 30		
12 45			06 45		
01 00 AM			07 00 AM		
01 15			07 15		
01 30			07 30		
01 45			07 45		
02 00 AM			08 00 AM		
02 15			08 15		
02 30			08 30		
02 45			08 45		
03 00 AM			09 00 AM		
03 15			09 15		
03 30			09 30		
03 45			09 45		
04 00 AM			10 00 AM		
04 15			10 15		
04 30			10 30		
04 45			10 45		
05 00 AM			11 00 AM		
05 15			11 15		
05 30			11 30		
05 45			11 45		

mini goals --> mini actions 5 - 15 min

DATE: _____   DAY: Mo Tu We Th Fr Sa Su

	GENTLE PLAN	TRACK DATA		GENTLE PLAN	TRACK DATA
12 00 PM			06 00 PM		
12 15			06 15		
12 30			06 30		
12 45			06 45		
01 00 PM			07 00 PM		
01 15			07 15		
01 30			07 30		
01 45			07 45		
02 00 PM			08 00 PM		
02 15			08 15		
02 30			08 30		
02 45			08 45		
03 00 PM			09 00 PM		
03 15			09 15		
03 30			09 30		
03 45			09 45		
04 00 PM			10 00 PM		
04 15			10 15		
04 30			10 30		
04 45			10 45		
05 00 PM			11 00 PM		
05 15			11 15		
05 30			11 30		
05 45			11 45		

I'm so proud of you for...

Country of the Day: I Channel the Energy of the Universe!

	GENTLE PLAN	TRACK DATA		GENTLE PLAN	TRACK DATA
12 00 AM			06 00 AM		
12 15			06 15		
12 30			06 30		
12 45			06 45		
01 00 AM			07 00 AM		
01 15			07 15		
01 30			07 30		
01 45			07 45		
02 00 AM			08 00 AM		
02 15			08 15		
02 30			08 30		
02 45			08 45		
03 00 AM			09 00 AM		
03 15			09 15		
03 30			09 30		
03 45			09 45		
04 00 AM			10 00 AM		
04 15			10 15		
04 30			10 30		
04 45			10 45		
05 00 AM			11 00 AM		
05 15			11 15		
05 30			11 30		
05 45			11 45		

mini goals --> mini actions 5 - 15 min

DATE: DAY: Mo Tu We Th Fr Sa Su

	GENTLE PLAN	TRACK DATA		GENTLE PLAN	TRACK DATA
12 00 PM			06 00 PM		
12 15			06 15		
12 30			06 30		
12 45			06 45		
01 00 PM			07 00 PM		
01 15			07 15		
01 30			07 30		
01 45			07 45		
02 00 PM			08 00 PM		
02 15			08 15		
02 30			08 30		
02 45			08 45		
03 00 PM			09 00 PM		
03 15			09 15		
03 30			09 30		
03 45			09 45		
04 00 PM			10 00 PM		
04 15			10 15		
04 30			10 30		
04 45			10 45		
05 00 PM			11 00 PM		
05 15			11 15		
05 30			11 30		
05 45			11 45		

I'm so proud of you for...

Country of the Day: I Channel the Energy of the Universe!

	GENTLE PLAN	TRACK DATA		GENTLE PLAN	TRACK DATA
12 00 AM			06 00 AM		
12 15			06 15		
12 30			06 30		
12 45			06 45		
01 00 AM			07 00 AM		
01 15			07 15		
01 30			07 30		
01 45			07 45		
02 00 AM			08 00 AM		
02 15			08 15		
02 30			08 30		
02 45			08 45		
03 00 AM			09 00 AM		
03 15			09 15		
03 30			09 30		
03 45			09 45		
04 00 AM			10 00 AM		
04 15			10 15		
04 30			10 30		
04 45			10 45		
05 00 AM			11 00 AM		
05 15			11 15		
05 30			11 30		
05 45			11 45		

mini goals --> mini actions 5 - 15 min

DATE: _____   DAY: Mo Tu We Th Fr Sa Su

	GENTLE PLAN	TRACK DATA		GENTLE PLAN	TRACK DATA
12 00 PM			06 00 PM		
12 15			06 15		
12 30			06 30		
12 45			06 45		
01 00 PM			07 00 PM		
01 15			07 15		
01 30			07 30		
01 45			07 45		
02 00 PM			08 00 PM		
02 15			08 15		
02 30			08 30		
02 45			08 45		
03 00 PM			09 00 PM		
03 15			09 15		
03 30			09 30		
03 45			09 45		
04 00 PM			10 00 PM		
04 15			10 15		
04 30			10 30		
04 45			10 45		
05 00 PM			11 00 PM		
05 15			11 15		
05 30			11 30		
05 45			11 45		

I'm so proud of you for...

Country of the Day: I Channel the Energy of the Universe!

	GENTLE PLAN	TRACK DATA		GENTLE PLAN	TRACK DATA
12 00 AM			06 00 AM		
12 15			06 15		
12 30			06 30		
12 45			06 45		
01 00 AM			07 00 AM		
01 15			07 15		
01 30			07 30		
01 45			07 45		
02 00 AM			08 00 AM		
02 15			08 15		
02 30			08 30		
02 45			08 45		
03 00 AM			09 00 AM		
03 15			09 15		
03 30			09 30		
03 45			09 45		
04 00 AM			10 00 AM		
04 15			10 15		
04 30			10 30		
04 45			10 45		
05 00 AM			11 00 AM		
05 15			11 15		
05 30			11 30		
05 45			11 45		

mini goals --> mini actions 5 - 15 min

DATE: DAY: Mo   Tu   We   Th   Fr   Sa   Su

	GENTLE PLAN	TRACK DATA		GENTLE PLAN	TRACK DATA
12 00 PM			06 00 PM		
12 15			06 15		
12 30			06 30		
12 45			06 45		
01 00 PM			07 00 PM		
01 15			07 15		
01 30			07 30		
01 45			07 45		
02 00 PM			08 00 PM		
02 15			08 15		
02 30			08 30		
02 45			08 45		
03 00 PM			09 00 PM		
03 15			09 15		
03 30			09 30		
03 45			09 45		
04 00 PM			10 00 PM		
04 15			10 15		
04 30			10 30		
04 45			10 45		
05 00 PM			11 00 PM		
05 15			11 15		
05 30			11 30		
05 45			11 45		

I'm so proud of you for...

Country of the Day: I Channel the Energy of the Universe!

	GENTLE PLAN	TRACK DATA		GENTLE PLAN	TRACK DATA
12 00 AM			06 00 AM		
12 15			06 15		
12 30			06 30		
12 45			06 45		
01 00 AM			07 00 AM		
01 15			07 15		
01 30			07 30		
01 45			07 45		
02 00 AM			08 00 AM		
02 15			08 15		
02 30			08 30		
02 45			08 45		
03 00 AM			09 00 AM		
03 15			09 15		
03 30			09 30		
03 45			09 45		
04 00 AM			10 00 AM		
04 15			10 15		
04 30			10 30		
04 45			10 45		
05 00 AM			11 00 AM		
05 15			11 15		
05 30			11 30		
05 45			11 45		

mini goals --> mini actions 5 - 15 min

DATE: DAY: Mo Tu We Th Fr Sa Su

	GENTLE PLAN	TRACK DATA		GENTLE PLAN	TRACK DATA
12 00 PM			06 00 PM		
12 15			06 15		
12 30			06 30		
12 45			06 45		
01 00 PM			07 00 PM		
01 15			07 15		
01 30			07 30		
01 45			07 45		
02 00 PM			08 00 PM		
02 15			08 15		
02 30			08 30		
02 45			08 45		
03 00 PM			09 00 PM		
03 15			09 15		
03 30			09 30		
03 45			09 45		
04 00 PM			10 00 PM		
04 15			10 15		
04 30			10 30		
04 45			10 45		
05 00 PM			11 00 PM		
05 15			11 15		
05 30			11 30		
05 45			11 45		

I'm so proud of you for...

GENTLE WEEK 3

You are already a third of the way through this planner. Wonderful!

Keep doing what you're doing. Practice your balance and alignment in the ebb and flow between the data tracking and gentle planning. Gentleness. Investigation. Read and re-read the 'How Do I Use This Planner?' and 'Universe-Supported' sections as many times as are helpful. Have you skipped ahead to the 'Country of the Day' and 'Guided Meditation'? It's okay to skip around this planner as much as you want. Enjoy. You're doing great. I'm so proud of you.

Country of the Day: I Channel the Energy of the Universe!

	GENTLE PLAN	TRACK DATA		GENTLE PLAN	TRACK DATA
12 00 AM			06 00 AM		
12 15			06 15		
12 30			06 30		
12 45			06 45		
01 00 AM			07 00 AM		
01 15			07 15		
01 30			07 30		
01 45			07 45		
02 00 AM			08 00 AM		
02 15			08 15		
02 30			08 30		
02 45			08 45		
03 00 AM			09 00 AM		
03 15			09 15		
03 30			09 30		
03 45			09 45		
04 00 AM			10 00 AM		
04 15			10 15		
04 30			10 30		
04 45			10 45		
05 00 AM			11 00 AM		
05 15			11 15		
05 30			11 30		
05 45			11 45		

mini goals --> mini actions 5 - 15 min

DATE: DAY: Mo   Tu   We   Th   Fr   Sa   Su

	GENTLE PLAN	TRACK DATA		GENTLE PLAN	TRACK DATA
12 00 PM			06 00 PM		
12 15			06 15		
12 30			06 30		
12 45			06 45		
01 00 PM			07 00 PM		
01 15			07 15		
01 30			07 30		
01 45			07 45		
02 00 PM			08 00 PM		
02 15			08 15		
02 30			08 30		
02 45			08 45		
03 00 PM			09 00 PM		
03 15			09 15		
03 30			09 30		
03 45			09 45		
04 00 PM			10 00 PM		
04 15			10 15		
04 30			10 30		
04 45			10 45		
05 00 PM			11 00 PM		
05 15			11 15		
05 30			11 30		
05 45			11 45		

I'm so proud of you for...

Country of the Day: I Channel the Energy of the Universe!

	GENTLE PLAN	TRACK DATA		GENTLE PLAN	TRACK DATA
12 00 AM			06 00 AM		
12 15			06 15		
12 30			06 30		
12 45			06 45		
01 00 AM			07 00 AM		
01 15			07 15		
01 30			07 30		
01 45			07 45		
02 00 AM			08 00 AM		
02 15			08 15		
02 30			08 30		
02 45			08 45		
03 00 AM			09 00 AM		
03 15			09 15		
03 30			09 30		
03 45			09 45		
04 00 AM			10 00 AM		
04 15			10 15		
04 30			10 30		
04 45			10 45		
05 00 AM			11 00 AM		
05 15			11 15		
05 30			11 30		
05 45			11 45		

mini goals --> mini actions 5 - 15 min

6-WEEK PLANNER + SPIRITUAL GUIDE = DAILY FREEDOM · 103

DATE: _____ DAY: Mo Tu We Th Fr Sa Su

GENTLE PLAN	TRACK DATA		GENTLE PLAN	TRACK DATA
12 00 PM		06 00 PM		
12 15		06 15		
12 30		06 30		
12 45		06 45		
01 00 PM		07 00 PM		
01 15		07 15		
01 30		07 30		
01 45		07 45		
02 00 PM		08 00 PM		
02 15		08 15		
02 30		08 30		
02 45		08 45		
03 00 PM		09 00 PM		
03 15		09 15		
03 30		09 30		
03 45		09 45		
04 00 PM		10 00 PM		
04 15		10 15		
04 30		10 30		
04 45		10 45		
05 00 PM		11 00 PM		
05 15		11 15		
05 30		11 30		
05 45		11 45		

I'm so proud of you for...

Country of the Day: I Channel the Energy of the Universe!

	GENTLE PLAN	TRACK DATA		GENTLE PLAN	TRACK DATA
12 00 AM			06 00 AM		
12 15			06 15		
12 30			06 30		
12 45			06 45		
01 00 AM			07 00 AM		
01 15			07 15		
01 30			07 30		
01 45			07 45		
02 00 AM			08 00 AM		
02 15			08 15		
02 30			08 30		
02 45			08 45		
03 00 AM			09 00 AM		
03 15			09 15		
03 30			09 30		
03 45			09 45		
04 00 AM			10 00 AM		
04 15			10 15		
04 30			10 30		
04 45			10 45		
05 00 AM			11 00 AM		
05 15			11 15		
05 30			11 30		
05 45			11 45		

mini goals --> mini actions 5 - 15 min

DATE: DAY: Mo Tu We Th Fr Sa Su

	GENTLE PLAN	TRACK DATA		GENTLE PLAN	TRACK DATA
12 00 PM			06 00 PM		
12 15			06 15		
12 30			06 30		
12 45			06 45		
01 00 PM			07 00 PM		
01 15			07 15		
01 30			07 30		
01 45			07 45		
02 00 PM			08 00 PM		
02 15			08 15		
02 30			08 30		
02 45			08 45		
03 00 PM			09 00 PM		
03 15			09 15		
03 30			09 30		
03 45			09 45		
04 00 PM			10 00 PM		
04 15			10 15		
04 30			10 30		
04 45			10 45		
05 00 PM			11 00 PM		
05 15			11 15		
05 30			11 30		
05 45			11 45		

I'm so proud of you for...

Country of the Day: I Channel the Energy of the Universe!

	GENTLE PLAN	TRACK DATA		GENTLE PLAN	TRACK DATA
12 00 AM			06 00 AM		
12 15			06 15		
12 30			06 30		
12 45			06 45		
01 00 AM			07 00 AM		
01 15			07 15		
01 30			07 30		
01 45			07 45		
02 00 AM			08 00 AM		
02 15			08 15		
02 30			08 30		
02 45			08 45		
03 00 AM			09 00 AM		
03 15			09 15		
03 30			09 30		
03 45			09 45		
04 00 AM			10 00 AM		
04 15			10 15		
04 30			10 30		
04 45			10 45		
05 00 AM			11 00 AM		
05 15			11 15		
05 30			11 30		
05 45			11 45		

mini goals --> mini actions 5 - 15 min

DATE: DAY: Mo Tu We Th Fr Sa Su

	GENTLE PLAN	TRACK DATA		GENTLE PLAN	TRACK DATA
12 00 PM			06 00 PM		
12 15			06 15		
12 30			06 30		
12 45			06 45		
01 00 PM			07 00 PM		
01 15			07 15		
01 30			07 30		
01 45			07 45		
02 00 PM			08 00 PM		
02 15			08 15		
02 30			08 30		
02 45			08 45		
03 00 PM			09 00 PM		
03 15			09 15		
03 30			09 30		
03 45			09 45		
04 00 PM			10 00 PM		
04 15			10 15		
04 30			10 30		
04 45			10 45		
05 00 PM			11 00 PM		
05 15			11 15		
05 30			11 30		
05 45			11 45		

I'm so proud of you for...

Country of the Day: I Channel the Energy of the Universe!

	GENTLE PLAN	TRACK DATA		GENTLE PLAN	TRACK DATA
12 00 AM			06 00 AM		
12 15			06 15		
12 30			06 30		
12 45			06 45		
01 00 AM			07 00 AM		
01 15			07 15		
01 30			07 30		
01 45			07 45		
02 00 AM			08 00 AM		
02 15			08 15		
02 30			08 30		
02 45			08 45		
03 00 AM			09 00 AM		
03 15			09 15		
03 30			09 30		
03 45			09 45		
04 00 AM			10 00 AM		
04 15			10 15		
04 30			10 30		
04 45			10 45		
05 00 AM			11 00 AM		
05 15			11 15		
05 30			11 30		
05 45			11 45		

mini goals --> mini actions 5 - 15 min

DATE: DAY: Mo Tu We Th Fr Sa Su

	GENTLE PLAN	TRACK DATA		GENTLE PLAN	TRACK DATA
12 00 PM			06 00 PM		
12 15			06 15		
12 30			06 30		
12 45			06 45		
01 00 PM			07 00 PM		
01 15			07 15		
01 30			07 30		
01 45			07 45		
02 00 PM			08 00 PM		
02 15			08 15		
02 30			08 30		
02 45			08 45		
03 00 PM			09 00 PM		
03 15			09 15		
03 30			09 30		
03 45			09 45		
04 00 PM			10 00 PM		
04 15			10 15		
04 30			10 30		
04 45			10 45		
05 00 PM			11 00 PM		
05 15			11 15		
05 30			11 30		
05 45			11 45		

I'm so proud of you for...

Country of the Day: I Channel the Energy of the Universe!

	GENTLE PLAN	TRACK DATA		GENTLE PLAN	TRACK DATA
12 00 AM			06 00 AM		
12 15			06 15		
12 30			06 30		
12 45			06 45		
01 00 AM			07 00 AM		
01 15			07 15		
01 30			07 30		
01 45			07 45		
02 00 AM			08 00 AM		
02 15			08 15		
02 30			08 30		
02 45			08 45		
03 00 AM			09 00 AM		
03 15			09 15		
03 30			09 30		
03 45			09 45		
04 00 AM			10 00 AM		
04 15			10 15		
04 30			10 30		
04 45			10 45		
05 00 AM			11 00 AM		
05 15			11 15		
05 30			11 30		
05 45			11 45		

mini goals -->   mini actions 5 - 15 min

DATE: DAY: Mo Tu We Th Fr Sa Su

	GENTLE PLAN	TRACK DATA		GENTLE PLAN	TRACK DATA
12 00 PM			06 00 PM		
12 15			06 15		
12 30			06 30		
12 45			06 45		
01 00 PM			07 00 PM		
01 15			07 15		
01 30			07 30		
01 45			07 45		
02 00 PM			08 00 PM		
02 15			08 15		
02 30			08 30		
02 45			08 45		
03 00 PM			09 00 PM		
03 15			09 15		
03 30			09 30		
03 45			09 45		
04 00 PM			10 00 PM		
04 15			10 15		
04 30			10 30		
04 45			10 45		
05 00 PM			11 00 PM		
05 15			11 15		
05 30			11 30		
05 45			11 45		

I'm so proud of you for...

Country of the Day: I Channel the Energy of the Universe!

	GENTLE PLAN	TRACK DATA		GENTLE PLAN	TRACK DATA
12 00 AM			06 00 AM		
12 15			06 15		
12 30			06 30		
12 45			06 45		
01 00 AM			07 00 AM		
01 15			07 15		
01 30			07 30		
01 45			07 45		
02 00 AM			08 00 AM		
02 15			08 15		
02 30			08 30		
02 45			08 45		
03 00 AM			09 00 AM		
03 15			09 15		
03 30			09 30		
03 45			09 45		
04 00 AM			10 00 AM		
04 15			10 15		
04 30			10 30		
04 45			10 45		
05 00 AM			11 00 AM		
05 15			11 15		
05 30			11 30		
05 45			11 45		

mini goals --> mini actions 5 - 15 min

DATE: DAY: Mo   Tu   We   Th   Fr   Sa   Su

	GENTLE PLAN	TRACK DATA		GENTLE PLAN	TRACK DATA
12 00 PM			06 00 PM		
12 15			06 15		
12 30			06 30		
12 45			06 45		
01 00 PM			07 00 PM		
01 15			07 15		
01 30			07 30		
01 45			07 45		
02 00 PM			08 00 PM		
02 15			08 15		
02 30			08 30		
02 45			08 45		
03 00 PM			09 00 PM		
03 15			09 15		
03 30			09 30		
03 45			09 45		
04 00 PM			10 00 PM		
04 15			10 15		
04 30			10 30		
04 45			10 45		
05 00 PM			11 00 PM		
05 15			11 15		
05 30			11 30		
05 45			11 45		

I'm so proud of you for...

GENTLE WEEK 4

You are already halfway through this planner. Wonderful!

Keep doing what you're doing. Practice your balance and alignment in the ebb and flow between the data tracking and gentle planning. Gentleness. Investigation. Read and re-read the 'How Do I Use This Planner?' and 'Universe-Supported' sections as many times as are helpful. Have you skipped ahead to the 'Country of the Day' and 'Guided Meditation'? It's okay to skip around this planner as much as you want. Enjoy. You're doing great. I'm so proud of you.

Country of the Day: I Channel the Energy of the Universe!

	GENTLE PLAN	TRACK DATA		GENTLE PLAN	TRACK DATA
12 00 AM			06 00 AM		
12 15			06 15		
12 30			06 30		
12 45			06 45		
01 00 AM			07 00 AM		
01 15			07 15		
01 30			07 30		
01 45			07 45		
02 00 AM			08 00 AM		
02 15			08 15		
02 30			08 30		
02 45			08 45		
03 00 AM			09 00 AM		
03 15			09 15		
03 30			09 30		
03 45			09 45		
04 00 AM			10 00 AM		
04 15			10 15		
04 30			10 30		
04 45			10 45		
05 00 AM			11 00 AM		
05 15			11 15		
05 30			11 30		
05 45			11 45		

mini goals --> mini actions 5 - 15 min

DATE: _____   DAY: Mo Tu We Th Fr Sa Su

	GENTLE PLAN	TRACK DATA		GENTLE PLAN	TRACK DATA
12 00 PM			06 00 PM		
12 15			06 15		
12 30			06 30		
12 45			06 45		
01 00 PM			07 00 PM		
01 15			07 15		
01 30			07 30		
01 45			07 45		
02 00 PM			08 00 PM		
02 15			08 15		
02 30			08 30		
02 45			08 45		
03 00 PM			09 00 PM		
03 15			09 15		
03 30			09 30		
03 45			09 45		
04 00 PM			10 00 PM		
04 15			10 15		
04 30			10 30		
04 45			10 45		
05 00 PM			11 00 PM		
05 15			11 15		
05 30			11 30		
05 45			11 45		

I'm so proud of you for...

Country of the Day: I Channel the Energy of the Universe!

	GENTLE PLAN	TRACK DATA		GENTLE PLAN	TRACK DATA
12 00 AM			06 00 AM		
12 15			06 15		
12 30			06 30		
12 45			06 45		
01 00 AM			07 00 AM		
01 15			07 15		
01 30			07 30		
01 45			07 45		
02 00 AM			08 00 AM		
02 15			08 15		
02 30			08 30		
02 45			08 45		
03 00 AM			09 00 AM		
03 15			09 15		
03 30			09 30		
03 45			09 45		
04 00 AM			10 00 AM		
04 15			10 15		
04 30			10 30		
04 45			10 45		
05 00 AM			11 00 AM		
05 15			11 15		
05 30			11 30		
05 45			11 45		

mini goals --> mini actions 5 - 15 min

DATE: DAY: Mo   Tu   We   Th   Fr   Sa   Su

	GENTLE PLAN	TRACK DATA		GENTLE PLAN	TRACK DATA
12 00 PM			06 00 PM		
12 15			06 15		
12 30			06 30		
12 45			06 45		
01 00 PM			07 00 PM		
01 15			07 15		
01 30			07 30		
01 45			07 45		
02 00 PM			08 00 PM		
02 15			08 15		
02 30			08 30		
02 45			08 45		
03 00 PM			09 00 PM		
03 15			09 15		
03 30			09 30		
03 45			09 45		
04 00 PM			10 00 PM		
04 15			10 15		
04 30			10 30		
04 45			10 45		
05 00 PM			11 00 PM		
05 15			11 15		
05 30			11 30		
05 45			11 45		

I'm so proud of you for...

Country of the Day: I Channel the Energy of the Universe!

	GENTLE PLAN	TRACK DATA		GENTLE PLAN	TRACK DATA
12 00 AM			06 00 AM		
12 15			06 15		
12 30			06 30		
12 45			06 45		
01 00 AM			07 00 AM		
01 15			07 15		
01 30			07 30		
01 45			07 45		
02 00 AM			08 00 AM		
02 15			08 15		
02 30			08 30		
02 45			08 45		
03 00 AM			09 00 AM		
03 15			09 15		
03 30			09 30		
03 45			09 45		
04 00 AM			10 00 AM		
04 15			10 15		
04 30			10 30		
04 45			10 45		
05 00 AM			11 00 AM		
05 15			11 15		
05 30			11 30		
05 45			11 45		

mini goals --> mini actions 5 - 15 min

DATE: DAY: Mo   Tu   We   Th   Fr   Sa   Su

	GENTLE PLAN	TRACK DATA		GENTLE PLAN	TRACK DATA
12 00 PM			06 00 PM		
12 15			06 15		
12 30			06 30		
12 45			06 45		
01 00 PM			07 00 PM		
01 15			07 15		
01 30			07 30		
01 45			07 45		
02 00 PM			08 00 PM		
02 15			08 15		
02 30			08 30		
02 45			08 45		
03 00 PM			09 00 PM		
03 15			09 15		
03 30			09 30		
03 45			09 45		
04 00 PM			10 00 PM		
04 15			10 15		
04 30			10 30		
04 45			10 45		
05 00 PM			11 00 PM		
05 15			11 15		
05 30			11 30		
05 45			11 45		

I'm so proud of you for...

Country of the Day: I Channel the Energy of the Universe!

	GENTLE PLAN	TRACK DATA		GENTLE PLAN	TRACK DATA
12 00 AM			06 00 AM		
12 15			06 15		
12 30			06 30		
12 45			06 45		
01 00 AM			07 00 AM		
01 15			07 15		
01 30			07 30		
01 45			07 45		
02 00 AM			08 00 AM		
02 15			08 15		
02 30			08 30		
02 45			08 45		
03 00 AM			09 00 AM		
03 15			09 15		
03 30			09 30		
03 45			09 45		
04 00 AM			10 00 AM		
04 15			10 15		
04 30			10 30		
04 45			10 45		
05 00 AM			11 00 AM		
05 15			11 15		
05 30			11 30		
05 45			11 45		

mini goals --> mini actions 5 - 15 min

DATE: _____   DAY: Mo Tu We Th Fr Sa Su

	GENTLE PLAN	TRACK DATA		GENTLE PLAN	TRACK DATA
12 00 PM			06 00 PM		
12 15			06 15		
12 30			06 30		
12 45			06 45		
01 00 PM			07 00 PM		
01 15			07 15		
01 30			07 30		
01 45			07 45		
02 00 PM			08 00 PM		
02 15			08 15		
02 30			08 30		
02 45			08 45		
03 00 PM			09 00 PM		
03 15			09 15		
03 30			09 30		
03 45			09 45		
04 00 PM			10 00 PM		
04 15			10 15		
04 30			10 30		
04 45			10 45		
05 00 PM			11 00 PM		
05 15			11 15		
05 30			11 30		
05 45			11 45		

I'm so proud of you for...

Country of the Day: I Channel the Energy of the Universe!

	GENTLE PLAN	TRACK DATA		GENTLE PLAN	TRACK DATA
12 00 AM			06 00 AM		
12 15			06 15		
12 30			06 30		
12 45			06 45		
01 00 AM			07 00 AM		
01 15			07 15		
01 30			07 30		
01 45			07 45		
02 00 AM			08 00 AM		
02 15			08 15		
02 30			08 30		
02 45			08 45		
03 00 AM			09 00 AM		
03 15			09 15		
03 30			09 30		
03 45			09 45		
04 00 AM			10 00 AM		
04 15			10 15		
04 30			10 30		
04 45			10 45		
05 00 AM			11 00 AM		
05 15			11 15		
05 30			11 30		
05 45			11 45		

mini goals --> mini actions 5 - 15 min

DATE: _____   DAY: Mo Tu We Th Fr Sa Su

	GENTLE PLAN	TRACK DATA		GENTLE PLAN	TRACK DATA
12 00 PM			06 00 PM		
12 15			06 15		
12 30			06 30		
12 45			06 45		
01 00 PM			07 00 PM		
01 15			07 15		
01 30			07 30		
01 45			07 45		
02 00 PM			08 00 PM		
02 15			08 15		
02 30			08 30		
02 45			08 45		
03 00 PM			09 00 PM		
03 15			09 15		
03 30			09 30		
03 45			09 45		
04 00 PM			10 00 PM		
04 15			10 15		
04 30			10 30		
04 45			10 45		
05 00 PM			11 00 PM		
05 15			11 15		
05 30			11 30		
05 45			11 45		

I'm so proud of you for...

Country of the Day: I Channel the Energy of the Universe!

	GENTLE PLAN	TRACK DATA		GENTLE PLAN	TRACK DATA
12 00 AM			06 00 AM		
12 15			06 15		
12 30			06 30		
12 45			06 45		
01 00 AM			07 00 AM		
01 15			07 15		
01 30			07 30		
01 45			07 45		
02 00 AM			08 00 AM		
02 15			08 15		
02 30			08 30		
02 45			08 45		
03 00 AM			09 00 AM		
03 15			09 15		
03 30			09 30		
03 45			09 45		
04 00 AM			10 00 AM		
04 15			10 15		
04 30			10 30		
04 45			10 45		
05 00 AM			11 00 AM		
05 15			11 15		
05 30			11 30		
05 45			11 45		

mini goals --> mini actions 5 - 15 min

DATE: DAY: Mo   Tu   We   Th   Fr   Sa   Su

	GENTLE PLAN	TRACK DATA		GENTLE PLAN	TRACK DATA
12 00 PM			06 00 PM		
12 15			06 15		
12 30			06 30		
12 45			06 45		
01 00 PM			07 00 PM		
01 15			07 15		
01 30			07 30		
01 45			07 45		
02 00 PM			08 00 PM		
02 15			08 15		
02 30			08 30		
02 45			08 45		
03 00 PM			09 00 PM		
03 15			09 15		
03 30			09 30		
03 45			09 45		
04 00 PM			10 00 PM		
04 15			10 15		
04 30			10 30		
04 45			10 45		
05 00 PM			11 00 PM		
05 15			11 15		
05 30			11 30		
05 45			11 45		

I'm so proud of you for...

Country of the Day: I Channel the Energy of the Universe!

	GENTLE PLAN	TRACK DATA		GENTLE PLAN	TRACK DATA
12 00 AM			06 00 AM		
12 15			06 15		
12 30			06 30		
12 45			06 45		
01 00 AM			07 00 AM		
01 15			07 15		
01 30			07 30		
01 45			07 45		
02 00 AM			08 00 AM		
02 15			08 15		
02 30			08 30		
02 45			08 45		
03 00 AM			09 00 AM		
03 15			09 15		
03 30			09 30		
03 45			09 45		
04 00 AM			10 00 AM		
04 15			10 15		
04 30			10 30		
04 45			10 45		
05 00 AM			11 00 AM		
05 15			11 15		
05 30			11 30		
05 45			11 45		

mini goals --> mini actions 5 - 15 min

DATE: DAY: Mo Tu We Th Fr Sa Su

	GENTLE PLAN	TRACK DATA		GENTLE PLAN	TRACK DATA
12 00 PM			06 00 PM		
12 15			06 15		
12 30			06 30		
12 45			06 45		
01 00 PM			07 00 PM		
01 15			07 15		
01 30			07 30		
01 45			07 45		
02 00 PM			08 00 PM		
02 15			08 15		
02 30			08 30		
02 45			08 45		
03 00 PM			09 00 PM		
03 15			09 15		
03 30			09 30		
03 45			09 45		
04 00 PM			10 00 PM		
04 15			10 15		
04 30			10 30		
04 45			10 45		
05 00 PM			11 00 PM		
05 15			11 15		
05 30			11 30		
05 45			11 45		

I'm so proud of you for...

GENTLE WEEK 5

Can you believe it is already Week 5? Wonderful!

Keep doing what you're doing. Practice your balance and alignment in the ebb and flow between the data tracking and gentle planning. Gentleness. Investigation. Read and re-read the 'How Do I Use This Planner?' and 'Universe-Supported' sections as many times as are helpful. Have you skipped ahead to the 'Country of the Day' and 'Guided Meditation'? It's okay to skip around this planner as much as you want. Enjoy. You're doing great. I'm so proud of you.

Country of the Day: I Channel the Energy of the Universe!

	GENTLE PLAN	TRACK DATA		GENTLE PLAN	TRACK DATA
12 00 AM			06 00 AM		
12 15			06 15		
12 30			06 30		
12 45			06 45		
01 00 AM			07 00 AM		
01 15			07 15		
01 30			07 30		
01 45			07 45		
02 00 AM			08 00 AM		
02 15			08 15		
02 30			08 30		
02 45			08 45		
03 00 AM			09 00 AM		
03 15			09 15		
03 30			09 30		
03 45			09 45		
04 00 AM			10 00 AM		
04 15			10 15		
04 30			10 30		
04 45			10 45		
05 00 AM			11 00 AM		
05 15			11 15		
05 30			11 30		
05 45			11 45		

mini goals --> mini actions 5 - 15 min

DATE: _____   DAY: Mo Tu We Th Fr Sa Su

GENTLE PLAN	TRACK DATA		GENTLE PLAN	TRACK DATA
12 00 PM		06 00 PM		
12 15		06 15		
12 30		06 30		
12 45		06 45		
01 00 PM		07 00 PM		
01 15		07 15		
01 30		07 30		
01 45		07 45		
02 00 PM		08 00 PM		
02 15		08 15		
02 30		08 30		
02 45		08 45		
03 00 PM		09 00 PM		
03 15		09 15		
03 30		09 30		
03 45		09 45		
04 00 PM		10 00 PM		
04 15		10 15		
04 30		10 30		
04 45		10 45		
05 00 PM		11 00 PM		
05 15		11 15		
05 30		11 30		
05 45		11 45		

I'm so proud of you for...

Country of the Day: I Channel the Energy of the Universe!

	GENTLE PLAN	TRACK DATA		GENTLE PLAN	TRACK DATA
12 00 AM			06 00 AM		
12 15			06 15		
12 30			06 30		
12 45			06 45		
01 00 AM			07 00 AM		
01 15			07 15		
01 30			07 30		
01 45			07 45		
02 00 AM			08 00 AM		
02 15			08 15		
02 30			08 30		
02 45			08 45		
03 00 AM			09 00 AM		
03 15			09 15		
03 30			09 30		
03 45			09 45		
04 00 AM			10 00 AM		
04 15			10 15		
04 30			10 30		
04 45			10 45		
05 00 AM			11 00 AM		
05 15			11 15		
05 30			11 30		
05 45			11 45		

mini goals --> mini actions 5 - 15 min

DATE: DAY: Mo   Tu   We   Th   Fr   Sa   Su

	GENTLE PLAN	TRACK DATA		GENTLE PLAN	TRACK DATA
12 00 PM			06 00 PM		
12 15			06 15		
12 30			06 30		
12 45			06 45		
01 00 PM			07 00 PM		
01 15			07 15		
01 30			07 30		
01 45			07 45		
02 00 PM			08 00 PM		
02 15			08 15		
02 30			08 30		
02 45			08 45		
03 00 PM			09 00 PM		
03 15			09 15		
03 30			09 30		
03 45			09 45		
04 00 PM			10 00 PM		
04 15			10 15		
04 30			10 30		
04 45			10 45		
05 00 PM			11 00 PM		
05 15			11 15		
05 30			11 30		
05 45			11 45		

I'm so proud of you for...

Country of the Day: I Channel the Energy of the Universe!

	GENTLE PLAN	TRACK DATA		GENTLE PLAN	TRACK DATA
12 00 AM			06 00 AM		
12 15			06 15		
12 30			06 30		
12 45			06 45		
01 00 AM			07 00 AM		
01 15			07 15		
01 30			07 30		
01 45			07 45		
02 00 AM			08 00 AM		
02 15			08 15		
02 30			08 30		
02 45			08 45		
03 00 AM			09 00 AM		
03 15			09 15		
03 30			09 30		
03 45			09 45		
04 00 AM			10 00 AM		
04 15			10 15		
04 30			10 30		
04 45			10 45		
05 00 AM			11 00 AM		
05 15			11 15		
05 30			11 30		
05 45			11 45		

mini goals --> mini actions 5 - 15 min

DATE: _____ DAY: Mo Tu We Th Fr Sa Su

	GENTLE PLAN	TRACK DATA		GENTLE PLAN	TRACK DATA
12 00 PM			06 00 PM		
12 15			06 15		
12 30			06 30		
12 45			06 45		
01 00 PM			07 00 PM		
01 15			07 15		
01 30			07 30		
01 45			07 45		
02 00 PM			08 00 PM		
02 15			08 15		
02 30			08 30		
02 45			08 45		
03 00 PM			09 00 PM		
03 15			09 15		
03 30			09 30		
03 45			09 45		
04 00 PM			10 00 PM		
04 15			10 15		
04 30			10 30		
04 45			10 45		
05 00 PM			11 00 PM		
05 15			11 15		
05 30			11 30		
05 45			11 45		

I'm so proud of you for...

Country of the Day: I Channel the Energy of the Universe!

	GENTLE PLAN	TRACK DATA		GENTLE PLAN	TRACK DATA
12 00 AM			06 00 AM		
12 15			06 15		
12 30			06 30		
12 45			06 45		
01 00 AM			07 00 AM		
01 15			07 15		
01 30			07 30		
01 45			07 45		
02 00 AM			08 00 AM		
02 15			08 15		
02 30			08 30		
02 45			08 45		
03 00 AM			09 00 AM		
03 15			09 15		
03 30			09 30		
03 45			09 45		
04 00 AM			10 00 AM		
04 15			10 15		
04 30			10 30		
04 45			10 45		
05 00 AM			11 00 AM		
05 15			11 15		
05 30			11 30		
05 45			11 45		

mini goals --> mini actions 5 - 15 min

DATE: _____   DAY: Mo Tu We Th Fr Sa Su

	GENTLE PLAN	TRACK DATA		GENTLE PLAN	TRACK DATA
12 00 PM			06 00 PM		
12 15			06 15		
12 30			06 30		
12 45			06 45		
01 00 PM			07 00 PM		
01 15			07 15		
01 30			07 30		
01 45			07 45		
02 00 PM			08 00 PM		
02 15			08 15		
02 30			08 30		
02 45			08 45		
03 00 PM			09 00 PM		
03 15			09 15		
03 30			09 30		
03 45			09 45		
04 00 PM			10 00 PM		
04 15			10 15		
04 30			10 30		
04 45			10 45		
05 00 PM			11 00 PM		
05 15			11 15		
05 30			11 30		
05 45			11 45		

I'm so proud of you for...

Country of the Day: I Channel the Energy of the Universe!

	GENTLE PLAN	TRACK DATA		GENTLE PLAN	TRACK DATA
12 00 AM			06 00 AM		
12 15			06 15		
12 30			06 30		
12 45			06 45		
01 00 AM			07 00 AM		
01 15			07 15		
01 30			07 30		
01 45			07 45		
02 00 AM			08 00 AM		
02 15			08 15		
02 30			08 30		
02 45			08 45		
03 00 AM			09 00 AM		
03 15			09 15		
03 30			09 30		
03 45			09 45		
04 00 AM			10 00 AM		
04 15			10 15		
04 30			10 30		
04 45			10 45		
05 00 AM			11 00 AM		
05 15			11 15		
05 30			11 30		
05 45			11 45		

mini goals --> mini actions 5 - 15 min

DATE: _____   DAY: Mo Tu We Th Fr Sa Su

	GENTLE PLAN	TRACK DATA		GENTLE PLAN	TRACK DATA
12 00 PM			06 00 PM		
12 15			06 15		
12 30			06 30		
12 45			06 45		
01 00 PM			07 00 PM		
01 15			07 15		
01 30			07 30		
01 45			07 45		
02 00 PM			08 00 PM		
02 15			08 15		
02 30			08 30		
02 45			08 45		
03 00 PM			09 00 PM		
03 15			09 15		
03 30			09 30		
03 45			09 45		
04 00 PM			10 00 PM		
04 15			10 15		
04 30			10 30		
04 45			10 45		
05 00 PM			11 00 PM		
05 15			11 15		
05 30			11 30		
05 45			11 45		

I'm so proud of you for...

Country of the Day: I Channel the Energy of the Universe!

	GENTLE PLAN	TRACK DATA		GENTLE PLAN	TRACK DATA
12 00 AM			06 00 AM		
12 15			06 15		
12 30			06 30		
12 45			06 45		
01 00 AM			07 00 AM		
01 15			07 15		
01 30			07 30		
01 45			07 45		
02 00 AM			08 00 AM		
02 15			08 15		
02 30			08 30		
02 45			08 45		
03 00 AM			09 00 AM		
03 15			09 15		
03 30			09 30		
03 45			09 45		
04 00 AM			10 00 AM		
04 15			10 15		
04 30			10 30		
04 45			10 45		
05 00 AM			11 00 AM		
05 15			11 15		
05 30			11 30		
05 45			11 45		

mini goals --> mini actions 5 - 15 min

DATE: DAY: Mo   Tu   We   Th   Fr   Sa   Su

	GENTLE PLAN	TRACK DATA		GENTLE PLAN	TRACK DATA
12 00 PM			06 00 PM		
12 15			06 15		
12 30			06 30		
12 45			06 45		
01 00 PM			07 00 PM		
01 15			07 15		
01 30			07 30		
01 45			07 45		
02 00 PM			08 00 PM		
02 15			08 15		
02 30			08 30		
02 45			08 45		
03 00 PM			09 00 PM		
03 15			09 15		
03 30			09 30		
03 45			09 45		
04 00 PM			10 00 PM		
04 15			10 15		
04 30			10 30		
04 45			10 45		
05 00 PM			11 00 PM		
05 15			11 15		
05 30			11 30		
05 45			11 45		

I'm so proud of you for...

Country of the Day: I Channel the Energy of the Universe!

	GENTLE PLAN	TRACK DATA			GENTLE PLAN	TRACK DATA
12 00 AM				06 00 AM		
12 15				06 15		
12 30				06 30		
12 45				06 45		
01 00 AM				07 00 AM		
01 15				07 15		
01 30				07 30		
01 45				07 45		
02 00 AM				08 00 AM		
02 15				08 15		
02 30				08 30		
02 45				08 45		
03 00 AM				09 00 AM		
03 15				09 15		
03 30				09 30		
03 45				09 45		
04 00 AM				10 00 AM		
04 15				10 15		
04 30				10 30		
04 45				10 45		
05 00 AM				11 00 AM		
05 15				11 15		
05 30				11 30		
05 45				11 45		

mini goals --> mini actions 5 - 15 min

DATE: DAY: Mo   Tu   We   Th   Fr   Sa   Su

	GENTLE PLAN	TRACK DATA		GENTLE PLAN	TRACK DATA
12 00 PM			06 00 PM		
12 15			06 15		
12 30			06 30		
12 45			06 45		
01 00 PM			07 00 PM		
01 15			07 15		
01 30			07 30		
01 45			07 45		
02 00 PM			08 00 PM		
02 15			08 15		
02 30			08 30		
02 45			08 45		
03 00 PM			09 00 PM		
03 15			09 15		
03 30			09 30		
03 45			09 45		
04 00 PM			10 00 PM		
04 15			10 15		
04 30			10 30		
04 45			10 45		
05 00 PM			11 00 PM		
05 15			11 15		
05 30			11 30		
05 45			11 45		

I'm so proud of you for...

GENTLE WEEK 6

You did it! You made it to the last week. I'm so proud of you!

Keep doing what you're doing. Practice your balance and alignment in the ebb and flow between the data tracking and gentle planning. Gentleness. Investigation. Read and re-read the 'How Do I Use This Planner?' and 'Universe-Supported' sections as many times as are helpful. Have you skipped ahead to the 'Country of the Day' and 'Guided Meditation'? It's okay to skip around this planner as much as you want. Enjoy. You're doing great. I'm so proud of you.

Country of the Day: I Channel the Energy of the Universe!

	GENTLE PLAN	TRACK DATA		GENTLE PLAN	TRACK DATA
12 00 AM			06 00 AM		
12 15			06 15		
12 30			06 30		
12 45			06 45		
01 00 AM			07 00 AM		
01 15			07 15		
01 30			07 30		
01 45			07 45		
02 00 AM			08 00 AM		
02 15			08 15		
02 30			08 30		
02 45			08 45		
03 00 AM			09 00 AM		
03 15			09 15		
03 30			09 30		
03 45			09 45		
04 00 AM			10 00 AM		
04 15			10 15		
04 30			10 30		
04 45			10 45		
05 00 AM			11 00 AM		
05 15			11 15		
05 30			11 30		
05 45			11 45		

mini goals --> mini actions 5 - 15 min

DATE: DAY: Mo   Tu   We   Th   Fr   Sa   Su

	GENTLE PLAN	TRACK DATA		GENTLE PLAN	TRACK DATA
12 00 PM			06 00 PM		
12 15			06 15		
12 30			06 30		
12 45			06 45		
01 00 PM			07 00 PM		
01 15			07 15		
01 30			07 30		
01 45			07 45		
02 00 PM			08 00 PM		
02 15			08 15		
02 30			08 30		
02 45			08 45		
03 00 PM			09 00 PM		
03 15			09 15		
03 30			09 30		
03 45			09 45		
04 00 PM			10 00 PM		
04 15			10 15		
04 30			10 30		
04 45			10 45		
05 00 PM			11 00 PM		
05 15			11 15		
05 30			11 30		
05 45			11 45		

I'm so proud of you for...

Country of the Day: I Channel the Energy of the Universe!

	GENTLE PLAN	TRACK DATA		GENTLE PLAN	TRACK DATA
12 00 AM			06 00 AM		
12 15			06 15		
12 30			06 30		
12 45			06 45		
01 00 AM			07 00 AM		
01 15			07 15		
01 30			07 30		
01 45			07 45		
02 00 AM			08 00 AM		
02 15			08 15		
02 30			08 30		
02 45			08 45		
03 00 AM			09 00 AM		
03 15			09 15		
03 30			09 30		
03 45			09 45		
04 00 AM			10 00 AM		
04 15			10 15		
04 30			10 30		
04 45			10 45		
05 00 AM			11 00 AM		
05 15			11 15		
05 30			11 30		
05 45			11 45		

mini goals --> mini actions 5 - 15 min

DATE: DAY: Mo Tu We Th Fr Sa Su

	GENTLE PLAN	TRACK DATA		GENTLE PLAN	TRACK DATA
12 00 PM			06 00 PM		
12 15			06 15		
12 30			06 30		
12 45			06 45		
01 00 PM			07 00 PM		
01 15			07 15		
01 30			07 30		
01 45			07 45		
02 00 PM			08 00 PM		
02 15			08 15		
02 30			08 30		
02 45			08 45		
03 00 PM			09 00 PM		
03 15			09 15		
03 30			09 30		
03 45			09 45		
04 00 PM			10 00 PM		
04 15			10 15		
04 30			10 30		
04 45			10 45		
05 00 PM			11 00 PM		
05 15			11 15		
05 30			11 30		
05 45			11 45		

I'm so proud of you for...

Country of the Day: I Channel the Energy of the Universe!

	GENTLE PLAN	TRACK DATA		GENTLE PLAN	TRACK DATA
12 00 AM			06 00 AM		
12 15			06 15		
12 30			06 30		
12 45			06 45		
01 00 AM			07 00 AM		
01 15			07 15		
01 30			07 30		
01 45			07 45		
02 00 AM			08 00 AM		
02 15			08 15		
02 30			08 30		
02 45			08 45		
03 00 AM			09 00 AM		
03 15			09 15		
03 30			09 30		
03 45			09 45		
04 00 AM			10 00 AM		
04 15			10 15		
04 30			10 30		
04 45			10 45		
05 00 AM			11 00 AM		
05 15			11 15		
05 30			11 30		
05 45			11 45		

mini goals --> mini actions 5 - 15 min

DATE: DAY: Mo   Tu   We   Th   Fr   Sa   Su

	GENTLE PLAN	TRACK DATA		GENTLE PLAN	TRACK DATA
12 00 PM			06 00 PM		
12 15			06 15		
12 30			06 30		
12 45			06 45		
01 00 PM			07 00 PM		
01 15			07 15		
01 30			07 30		
01 45			07 45		
02 00 PM			08 00 PM		
02 15			08 15		
02 30			08 30		
02 45			08 45		
03 00 PM			09 00 PM		
03 15			09 15		
03 30			09 30		
03 45			09 45		
04 00 PM			10 00 PM		
04 15			10 15		
04 30			10 30		
04 45			10 45		
05 00 PM			11 00 PM		
05 15			11 15		
05 30			11 30		
05 45			11 45		

I'm so proud of you for...

Country of the Day: I Channel the Energy of the Universe!

	GENTLE PLAN	TRACK DATA		GENTLE PLAN	TRACK DATA
12 00 AM			06 00 AM		
12 15			06 15		
12 30			06 30		
12 45			06 45		
01 00 AM			07 00 AM		
01 15			07 15		
01 30			07 30		
01 45			07 45		
02 00 AM			08 00 AM		
02 15			08 15		
02 30			08 30		
02 45			08 45		
03 00 AM			09 00 AM		
03 15			09 15		
03 30			09 30		
03 45			09 45		
04 00 AM			10 00 AM		
04 15			10 15		
04 30			10 30		
04 45			10 45		
05 00 AM			11 00 AM		
05 15			11 15		
05 30			11 30		
05 45			11 45		

mini goals --> mini actions 5 - 15 min

DATE: DAY: Mo   Tu   We   Th   Fr   Sa   Su

	GENTLE PLAN	TRACK DATA		GENTLE PLAN	TRACK DATA
12 00 PM			06 00 PM		
12 15			06 15		
12 30			06 30		
12 45			06 45		
01 00 PM			07 00 PM		
01 15			07 15		
01 30			07 30		
01 45			07 45		
02 00 PM			08 00 PM		
02 15			08 15		
02 30			08 30		
02 45			08 45		
03 00 PM			09 00 PM		
03 15			09 15		
03 30			09 30		
03 45			09 45		
04 00 PM			10 00 PM		
04 15			10 15		
04 30			10 30		
04 45			10 45		
05 00 PM			11 00 PM		
05 15			11 15		
05 30			11 30		
05 45			11 45		

I'm so proud of you for...

Country of the Day: I Channel the Energy of the Universe!

	GENTLE PLAN	TRACK DATA		GENTLE PLAN	TRACK DATA
12 00 AM			06 00 AM		
12 15			06 15		
12 30			06 30		
12 45			06 45		
01 00 AM			07 00 AM		
01 15			07 15		
01 30			07 30		
01 45			07 45		
02 00 AM			08 00 AM		
02 15			08 15		
02 30			08 30		
02 45			08 45		
03 00 AM			09 00 AM		
03 15			09 15		
03 30			09 30		
03 45			09 45		
04 00 AM			10 00 AM		
04 15			10 15		
04 30			10 30		
04 45			10 45		
05 00 AM			11 00 AM		
05 15			11 15		
05 30			11 30		
05 45			11 45		

mini goals --> mini actions 5 - 15 min

DATE: DAY: Mo Tu We Th Fr Sa Su

	GENTLE PLAN	TRACK DATA		GENTLE PLAN	TRACK DATA
12 00 PM			06 00 PM		
12 15			06 15		
12 30			06 30		
12 45			06 45		
01 00 PM			07 00 PM		
01 15			07 15		
01 30			07 30		
01 45			07 45		
02 00 PM			08 00 PM		
02 15			08 15		
02 30			08 30		
02 45			08 45		
03 00 PM			09 00 PM		
03 15			09 15		
03 30			09 30		
03 45			09 45		
04 00 PM			10 00 PM		
04 15			10 15		
04 30			10 30		
04 45			10 45		
05 00 PM			11 00 PM		
05 15			11 15		
05 30			11 30		
05 45			11 45		

I'm so proud of you for...

Country of the Day: I Channel the Energy of the Universe!

	GENTLE PLAN	TRACK DATA		GENTLE PLAN	TRACK DATA
12 00 AM			06 00 AM		
12 15			06 15		
12 30			06 30		
12 45			06 45		
01 00 AM			07 00 AM		
01 15			07 15		
01 30			07 30		
01 45			07 45		
02 00 AM			08 00 AM		
02 15			08 15		
02 30			08 30		
02 45			08 45		
03 00 AM			09 00 AM		
03 15			09 15		
03 30			09 30		
03 45			09 45		
04 00 AM			10 00 AM		
04 15			10 15		
04 30			10 30		
04 45			10 45		
05 00 AM			11 00 AM		
05 15			11 15		
05 30			11 30		
05 45			11 45		

mini goals --> mini actions 5 - 15 min

DATE: DAY: Mo   Tu   We   Th   Fr   Sa   Su

	GENTLE PLAN	TRACK DATA		GENTLE PLAN	TRACK DATA
12 00 PM			06 00 PM		
12 15			06 15		
12 30			06 30		
12 45			06 45		
01 00 PM			07 00 PM		
01 15			07 15		
01 30			07 30		
01 45			07 45		
02 00 PM			08 00 PM		
02 15			08 15		
02 30			08 30		
02 45			08 45		
03 00 PM			09 00 PM		
03 15			09 15		
03 30			09 30		
03 45			09 45		
04 00 PM			10 00 PM		
04 15			10 15		
04 30			10 30		
04 45			10 45		
05 00 PM			11 00 PM		
05 15			11 15		
05 30			11 30		
05 45			11 45		

I'm so proud of you for...

Country of the Day: I Channel the Energy of the Universe!

	GENTLE PLAN	TRACK DATA		GENTLE PLAN	TRACK DATA
12 00 AM			06 00 AM		
12 15			06 15		
12 30			06 30		
12 45			06 45		
01 00 AM			07 00 AM		
01 15			07 15		
01 30			07 30		
01 45			07 45		
02 00 AM			08 00 AM		
02 15			08 15		
02 30			08 30		
02 45			08 45		
03 00 AM			09 00 AM		
03 15			09 15		
03 30			09 30		
03 45			09 45		
04 00 AM			10 00 AM		
04 15			10 15		
04 30			10 30		
04 45			10 45		
05 00 AM			11 00 AM		
05 15			11 15		
05 30			11 30		
05 45			11 45		

mini goals --> mini actions 5 - 15 min

DATE: DAY: Mo Tu We Th Fr Sa Su

	GENTLE PLAN	TRACK DATA		GENTLE PLAN	TRACK DATA
12 00 PM			06 00 PM		
12 15			06 15		
12 30			06 30		
12 45			06 45		
01 00 PM			07 00 PM		
01 15			07 15		
01 30			07 30		
01 45			07 45		
02 00 PM			08 00 PM		
02 15			08 15		
02 30			08 30		
02 45			08 45		
03 00 PM			09 00 PM		
03 15			09 15		
03 30			09 30		
03 45			09 45		
04 00 PM			10 00 PM		
04 15			10 15		
04 30			10 30		
04 45			10 45		
05 00 PM			11 00 PM		
05 15			11 15		
05 30			11 30		
05 45			11 45		

I'm so proud of you for...

GENTLE DATA

Congratulations on your new superpower of time! Perfectly imperfect; we celebrate progress here. Can you see the progress? I'm so proud of you. Not many people take willing actions to try something new, and you did! That's wonderful! Even if this was not your first time using this planner, this was a new 6-weeks, and I am still so proud of you!

Optional—Casual data observations about the past 6-weeks. As I flip through the pages, what do I see? Gentleness. Where have I made progress? What am I still challenged by? Where can I practice something different? What is working for me?

There are boxes here if you prefer those, or blank pages at the back of this planner.

GENTLENESS	GENTLENESS	GENTLENESS	GENTLENESS

GENTLENESS   GENTLENESS   GENTLENESS   GENTLENESS

GENTLENESS	GENTLENESS	GENTLENESS	GENTLENESS

GENTLENESS	GENTLENESS	GENTLENESS	GENTLENESS

GUIDED MEDITATION

I have noticed that when I get time-vague, it is often a trauma response to a trigger of some kind. I am no longer in my body at that point.

I wrote this meditation to reconnect with my body and my higher power. I invite you to try this guided meditation and evaluate if you feel differently before and after—as an experiment. Some options are—you can read it to yourself, read it to someone else, or record yourself reading it so you can listen to it later (which is what I do).

- Like a shopping cart with a wheel out of sync, meditation is a practice of re-aligning our thoughts towards the direction we want the cart to go in.
- If I feel comfortable, I am invited to close my eyes, or look at one specific spot on the floor.
- I re-adjust and sit in a relaxed, natural position. My arms and legs are uncrossed, signaling openness to a new experience.
- All the sounds I hear are neither good nor bad, they're just sounds; in one ear, out the other.
- Labels and thoughts come up about this—I see a windshield wiper, and choose to turn it on and lovingly clean my window of the now, and those judgments wipe away.
- *I breathe in Peace... I breathe out Tranquility...*
- I un-clench my jaw, allowing for space between my top and bottom teeth, and remove my tongue from the roof of my mouth.

I relax the space between my eyebrows, bringing gentleness to my face.

- I use the windshield wiper to wipe away any thoughts that come up about this.
- *I breathe in Space... I breathe out Hope...*
- If I want to, I gently bring my hands together in my lap or on my thighs, in a relaxed position. I move my hands together—each hand mirroring the other. I see a mirror held in front of a mirror, and the infinite mirrors now created in-between. I slowly bring my palms apart, keeping my fingertips touching; connected.
- *I breathe in Light... I breathe out Connection...*
- The space between my palms holds the Energy of the Universe, my Higher Power—unique to me, that flows in and through me.
- *I breathe in Abundance... I breathe out Gratitude...*
- Keeping my eyes closed or looking at the floor, I bring my awareness to my feet. The left toes, the right toes, I wiggle them playfully.
- I windshield-wiper away any thoughts that come up about playfulness.
- *I breathe in Playfulness... I breathe out Joy...*
- I bring my awareness up my shins, through the kneecaps, up my thighs. I relax my muscles. Beneath the skin and muscle is the bone—the anchoring force as I move throughout my day.
- I windshield wiper away any thoughts that come up about my body.
- *I breathe in Acceptance... I breathe out Strength...*
- I bring my awareness up my body, relaxing my muscles, and focus on my belly button—a gentle reminder my body was made to be nourished.
- *I breathe in Nourishment... I breathe out Gentleness...*

- Today, my body is a sacred home for my Higher Power.
- I windshield wiper away any thoughts that come up about this.
- Today I choose to nurture my body.
- *I breathe in Kindness... I breathe out Encouragement...*
- I bring my awareness up to my heart—it beats autonomously, as I sleep and as I am awake; the Energy Source of the Universe keeps it beating. I channel the Energy of the Universe.
- I windshield wiper away any thoughts that come up about this.
- *I breathe in a Heartbeat... I breathe out Steadiness...*
- I bring my awareness to my shoulders. I relax the muscles, knowing the weight of the world is not on them.
- I windshield wiper away any thoughts that come up about this.
- *I breathe in Relief... I breathe out Partnership...*
- I bring my awareness down my arms and relax my muscles as I go. I focus my attention to the energy that flows between my palms, in me and through me.
- I windshield wiper away any thoughts that come up about this.
- *I breathe in Spirit... I breathe out Empowerment...*
- My higher power is with me here, now. All I need to do to access this Energy Source is to breathe in... and breathe out. I always have access to this Infinite Energy Source, whenever I may choose.
- I windshield wiper away any thoughts that come up about this.
- *I breathe in Awareness... I breathe out Serenity...*
- The mirrors between my palms is the energy of my higher power. I open my hands slowly. I send energy out and I receive energy back. My hands rest open naturally.
- *I breathe in Energy... I breathe out Clarity ...*

- Keeping my physical eyes as they have been, I bring my awareness to my forehead, to the third eye, the space where my eyebrows and nose intersect.
- I windshield wiper away any thoughts that come up about this.
- *I breathe in Healing... I breathe out Restoration...*
- The "eye of wisdom" is the wisdom of my higher power that naturally flows through me; a direct lineage from my Energy Source and Supply. Wisdom is a spiritual connectedness.
- I windshield wiper away any thoughts that come up about this.
- *I breathe in Wisdom... I breathe out Vitality...*
- I am willing to let go of the chains that bind.
- I am willing to let go.
- Keeping my physical eyes as they have been, I open my third eye of spirituality. I can see what is in front of me. I can see through the back of my head and see what's behind me. I can look down through the eye of the Universe, and I can see me, here. I smile lovingly as I see me.
- I windshield wiper away any thoughts that come up about this.
- With my eye of wisdom open, I can rewind my day and see me as I got here. Rewinding further, and I see me today as I moved about before I got here. It is a fast rewind where I can see feelings, and I cannot hear any words. I smile as I see me. Rewinding... looking... seeing... smiling.
- I windshield wiper away any thoughts that come up about this.
- I see me as I woke up. I see me as I slept. I see me as I went through my day yesterday. Rewinding... looking... seeing... smiling. I see me and I smile, lovingly.
- I windshield wiper away any thoughts that come up about this.
- Like a DJ with turntables, I reverse the flow of the movie, and fast forward back through time, seeing me, and I smile, lovingly. I fast

forward back to this day as it started, I see me moving about, and I smile as I see me. I see the feelings and cannot hear the words. I fast forward back to here, now. I can look down through the eye of the Universe and I see me here now, and I smile, lovingly.

- I windshield wiper away any thoughts that come up about this.
- *I breathe in Sunlight... I breathe out Freedom.*
- I slowly reawaken my body back into the space. I channel the Energy of the Universe. I stretch as it feels natural. I open all my eyes, and smile.[4]

---

[4] If you have one hand, you can put your hand over your heart during the meditation prompts about hands. If you have no hands or cannot move them, you can focus your Energy on the Light that flows through you.

COUNTRY OF THE DAY

My list here has 257 countries[5], territories, and areas of land. This is a list of international 3-letter shipping codes[6], which I started from the Logistics and Performance Index (LPI) [7] which has 160 countries listed. I added from there more places that are not technically countries and still have their own distinct shipping code.

This list began in grad school getting my MBA when I was introduced to the LPI. My focus in my MBA was International Business and even saying that came with anxiety, feeling that I do not know enough countries out there in the world—especially to have a degree with the word 'International'.

So, I took the list and decided to learn about a country a day and began listing them on the top of my planner—turning this big, giant, scary goal into something do-able. I started to share with others what today's 'Country of the Day' was because I found joy in it, and other people seemed to enjoy it, too. If not for the countries themselves, but to experience that you can learn anything if you break it down into something small, like one-a-day.

Some days I write down the name and learn the name and let that be enough. Some days I look it up on Maps and find out where it is located. Some days I set the timer for 15 minutes and learn as much as I can about it. Some days I research random things about it and learn the way it is pronounced. What language do they speak? Which

---

[5] GBR is for The United Kingdom, which has 4 countries that I separated because they are each special
[6] ISO Alpha-3 Codes
[7] HTTPS://LPI.WORLDBANK.ORG/

side of the road do they drive on? Any topics that you are passionate about, I encourage you to research what their situation is in that country (i.e. LGBTQIA+, animal rights, politics, access to clean water and healthcare, natural resources, BIPOC equality, global warming, etc.). Some days I will check the weather there today. What is their prison system like? What currency do they use? I like to bring focus to that country for that day, even if it is only me that knows about it. That *does* matter and that *does* make a difference. Sending Energy or prayers there for that day. What time is it there right now? What immunizations would I need to travel there? Use this tool in whatever way amuses you and brings delight. It is an option available to you.

You also have permission to go in any order—A to Z, Z to A, or picking one randomly and crossing it off.

Code	Country
AFG	Afghanistan
ALA	Åland Islands
ALB	Albania
DZA	Algeria
ASM	American Samoa
AND	Andorra
AGO	Angola
AIA	Anguilla
ATA	Antarctica
ATG	Antigua and Barbuda
ARG	Argentina
ARM	Armenia
ABW	Aruba
AUS	Australia

AUT	Austria
AZE	Azerbaijan
RAA	Azores
BHS	Bahamas, The
BHR	Bahrain
BGD	Bangladesh
BRB	Barbados
BLR	Belarus
BEL	Belgium
BLZ	Belize
BEN	Benin
BMU	Bermuda
BTN	Bhutan
BOL	Bolivia

BES	Bonaire, St. Eustatius and Saba		CRI	Costa Rica
BIH	Bosnia and Herzegovina		CIV	Côte d'Ivoire
BWA	Botswana		HRV	Croatia
BVT	Bouvet Island		CUB	Cuba
BRA	Brazil		CUW	Curaçao
IOT	British Indian Ocean Territory		CYP	Cyprus
VGB	British Virgin Islands		CZE	Czechia
BRN	Brunei Darussalam		DNK	Denmark
BGR	Bulgaria		DJI	Djibouti
BFA	Burkina Faso		DMA	Dominica
BDI	Burundi		DOM	Dominican Republic
KHM	Cambodia		ECU	Ecuador
CMR	Cameroon		EGY	Egypt
CAN	Canada		SLV	El Salvador
CPV	Cape Verde		GBR	England
CYM	Cayman Islands		GNQ	Equatorial Guinea
CAF	Central African Republic		ERI	Eritrea
TCD	Chad		EST	Estonia
CHL	Chile		SWZ	Eswatini
CHN	China		ETH	Ethiopia
CXR	Christmas Island		FLK	Falkland Islands
CCK	Cocos (Keeling) Islands		FRO	Faroe Islands
COL	Colombia		FJI	Fiji
COM	Comoros		FIN	Finland
COG	Congo		FRA	France
COD	Congo, Dem. Rep.		GUF	French Guiana
COK	Cook Islands		PYF	French Polynesia
			ATF	French Southern Territories
			GAB	Gabon
			GMB	Gambia

GEO	Georgia		JEY	Jersey
DEU	Germany		JOR	Jordan
GHA	Ghana		KAZ	Kazakhstan
GIB	Gibraltar		KEN	Kenya
GRC	Greece		KIR	Kiribati
GRL	Greenland		PRK	Korea, North
GRD	Grenada		KOR	Korea, South
GLP	Guadeloupe		XXK	Kosovo
GUM	Guam		KWT	Kuwait
GTM	Guatemala		KGZ	Kyrgyzstan
GGY	Guernsey		LAO	Laos Rep.
GIN	Guinea		LVA	Latvia
GNB	Guinea-Bissau		LBN	Lebanon
GUY	Guyana		LSO	Lesotho
HTI	Haiti		LBR	Liberia
HMD	Heard and McDonald Islands		LBY	Libya
			LIE	Liechtenstein
HND	Honduras		LTU	Lithuania
HKG	Hong Kong		LUX	Luxembourg
HUN	Hungary		MAC	Macau
ISL	Iceland		MKD	Macedonia, North
IND	India		MDG	Madagascar
IDN	Indonesia		MWI	Malawi
IRN	Iran, Rep.		MYS	Malaysia
IRQ	Iraq		MDV	Maldives
IRL	Ireland		MLI	Mali
IMN	Isle of Man		MLT	Malta
ISR	Israel		MHL	Marshall Islands
ITA	Italy		MTQ	Martinique
JAM	Jamaica		MRT	Mauritania
JPN	Japan		MUS	Mauritius

MYT	Mayotte		PAN	Panama
MEX	Mexico		PNG	Papua New Guinea
FSM	Micronesia		PRY	Paraguay
MDA	Moldova Rep.		PER	Peru
MCO	Monaco		PHL	Philippines
MNG	Mongolia		PCN	Pitcairn Islands
MNE	Montenegro		POL	Poland
MSR	Montserrat		PRT	Portugal
MAR	Morocco		PRI	Puerto Rico
MOZ	Mozambique		QAT	Qatar
MMR	Myanmar		REU	Réunion
GBR	N. Ireland		ROU	Romania
NAM	Namibia		RUS	Russian Federation
NRU	Nauru		RWA	Rwanda
NPL	Nepal		SGS	S. Georgia and S. Sandwich Islands
NLD	Netherlands			
ANT	Netherlands Antilles		BLM	Saint Barthélemy
NCL	New Caledonia		SHN	Saint Helena, Ascension and Tristan da Cunha
NZL	New Zealand			
NIC	Nicaragua		KNA	Saint Kitts and Nevis
NER	Niger			
NGA	Nigeria		LCA	Saint Lucia
NIU	Niue		MAF	Saint Martin (French)
NFK	Norfolk Island		SPM	Saint Pierre and Miquelon
MNP	Northern Mariana Islands			
NOR	Norway		VCT	Saint Vincent and the Grenadines
OMN	Oman			
PAK	Pakistan		WSM	Samoa
PLW	Palau		SMR	San Marino
PSE	Palestine State		STP	São Tomé and Principe
			SAU	Saudi Arabia

GBR	Scotland		TGO	Togo
SEN	Senegal		TKL	Tokelau
SRB	Serbia		TON	Tonga
SCG	Serbia and Montenegro		TTO	Trinidad and Tobago
SYC	Seychelles		TUN	Tunisia
SLE	Sierra Leone		TUR	Turkey
SGP	Singapore		TKM	Turkmenistan
SXM	Sint Maarten (Dutch)		TCA	Turks and Caicos Islands
SVK	Slovakia		TUV	Tuvalu
SVN	Slovenia		UMI	U.S. Minor Outlying Islands
SLB	Solomon Islands		VIR	U.S. Virgin Islands
SOM	Somalia		UGA	Uganda
ZAF	South Africa		UKR	Ukraine
SSD	South Sudan		ARE	United Arab Emirates
ESP	Spain		GBR	United Kingdom
LKA	Sri Lanka		USA	United States
SDN	Sudan		URY	Uruguay
SUR	Suriname		UZB	Uzbekistan
SJM	Svalbard and Jan Mayen Islands		VUT	Vanuatu
SWE	Sweden		VAT	Vatican, Holy See
CHE	Switzerland		VEN	Venezuela
SYR	Syrian Arab Rep.		VNM	Viet Nam
TWN	Taiwan, Prov. of China		GBR	Wales
TJK	Tajikistan		WLF	Wallis and Futuna
TZA	Tanzania, United Rep.		ESH	Western Sahara
THA	Thailand		YEM	Yemen
TLS	Timor-Leste		ZMB	Zambia
			ZWE	Zimbabwe

UNIVERSE-SUPPORTED TEAM

In the event that as you gently observe your time, you spend your time in certain ways that you do not want for yourself and yet cannot seem to stop doing it—there is hope. I invite you to investigate some of these free programs if they jump out to you. There may be a team of support available to you that understand what you are going through and have found a solution.

ACA	Adult Children of Alcoholics & Dysfunctional Families	https://adultchildren.org/
AA	Alcoholics Anonymous	https://aa.org/
ABA	Anorexics & Bulimics Anonymous	https://aba12steps.org/
BDA	Business Debtors Anonymous	https://debtorsanonymous.org/
BUA	Business Underearners Anonymous	https://www.underearnersanonymous.org/
CLA	Clutterers Anonymous	https://clutterersanonymous.org/
CA	Cocaine Anonymous	https://ca.org/
CoDA	Co-Dependents Anonymous	https://coda.org/
CMA	Crystal Meth Anonymous	https://www.crystalmeth.org/
DA	Debtors Anonymous	https://debtorsanonymous.org/
Al Anon	Family & Friends of Alcoholics	https://al-anon.org/
GA	Gamblers Anonymous	http://www.gamblersanonymous.org
ITAA	Internet and Technology Addicts Anonymous	https://internetaddictsanonymous.org/
OSPA	Obsessive Skin Pickers Anonymous	https://www.osparecovery.org/
OA	Overeaters Anonymous	https://oa.org/
PA	Pills Anonymous	https://www.pillsanonymous.org/
RCA	Recovering Couples Anonymous	https://recovering-couples.org/
SAA	Sex Addicts Anonymous	https://saa-recovery.org/
SLAA	Sex and Love Addicts Anonymous	https://slaafws.org/
SIA	Survivors of Incest Anonymous	https://siawso.org/
UA	Underearners Anonymous	https://www.underearnersanonymous.org/
WA	Workaholics Anonymous	https://workaholics-anonymous.org/

ABOUT THE AUTHOR

Phoenix G., MBA—(she/her/they)—currently resides near Houston, Texas, USA. Thanks to this planner, she recently graduated with her MBA with a focus in International Business. Thanks to this planner, Phoenix is the creator, owner, and President of Sunshine Under the Trees, Corporation. Thanks to this planner, Phoenix does not have to wait for 'spare time' to do what she enjoys—living life with her many dogs and cats, raising Monarch butterflies, reading (via text-to-speech), power yoga, cake-decorating, jiu-jitsu, painting, sewing, creating, binge-watching, gardening, service work, sleeping, writing, swimming, walking the dogs, and being an advocate for those whose voices are muted. Instead of time getting away from her, now Phoenix enjoys using her time in whatever way she wants.

FREEDOM PAGES